Anchors and Sails
A Reading Program for Beginners

Bev Jaremko

Illustrated by
Jeanette Debusschere

Captus Press

Anchors and Sails: A Reading Program for Beginners

Copyright © 2001 by Bev Jaremko and Captus Press Inc.

Canadian Cataloguing in Publication Data

Jaremko, Bev, 1949–

ISBN 1–55322–020–X

   1. English language — Alphabet — Juvenile literature.
2. Reading (Preschool) I. Debusschere, Jeanette II. Title.

PE1155.J35 2001   4421'.1   C2001–903392–3

Captus Press Inc.
Mail: York University Campus
           4700 Keele Street
           North York, Ontario
           M3J 1P3
Telephone: (416) 736–5537
Fax: (416) 736–5793
Email: info@captus.com
Internet: www.captus.com

Canada ◆ We acknowledge the financial support of the Government of Canada through the Book Publishing Industry Development Program (BPIDP) for our publishing activities.

0 9 8 7 6 5 4 3 2 1
Printed in Canada

Preface

Enter Reading

I had been teaching secondary school for about four years when I started to notice a pattern. Many of my tall adult-looking kids were embarrassed to read aloud, and they shuffled restlessly, laughed and whispered inaudibly as if any reasonable and merciful teacher would please let them sit down.

For some time I thought it was shyness or a problem of one or two individuals only; but, talking with them one-on-one, I discovered a sadder revelation — many of them could barely read. Somehow, in this high-tech, computer literate, well-funded education system, they had fallen between the cracks and now were struggling in ways unimaginable. Not only did they get low marks in English, but also in Social Studies, Science, Geography, Legal Studies — in fact, in anything that required them to read. And that meant they even got low marks in Math, because they did not read the problems well, and low marks in any written part of Home Economics, Industrial Arts, and even Drama and Phys Ed.

Inability to read was standing in the way of their success in nearly all subjects. And what was worse for me to watch was that each of them understood that a long time ago and had made a mental leap to a horrible conclusion — 'I am stupid.' It was completely inaccurate; often, they were very smart. But they had not been taught well, and maybe someone, inadvertently, had also had the audacity to blame them and not the poor teaching, which was a heartbreak.

Whatever had happened back then, from it they leapt to another coping mechanism: 'I will hide this fact; I will mock the system, and not even try, because that way, no one will be able to see my problem.' Often, the poor readers fell into two groups — the loner, isolated kids, and the highly visible behaviour problems.

I did what I could to help these kids, but by age 16 many of them dropped out of school, a few entered the criminal justice system, a few got pregnant. I felt a kind of despair for them.

When my husband and I had our first son I watched him closely, and one day, when he was two, I had an idea while camping. It occurred to me that he already was interested in being read to, and in what the letters on the page were, and here was a chance I could use to save him the heartbreak of those kids I had taught. I would teach him to read before he even went to school.

I scoured the market to find material for this early instruction and was sad to see that there were many game books about the alphabet, and some audio and video and even computer games for young kids, but there was nothing that actually taught the skill, sequentially, from zero ability to, say, a grade three reading level. And I had figured out that I needed that, because my little son was no different from other kids, and that meant he was incredibly logical.

It would be very kind to show him how to put letters together to make words. But it would be very cruel to confuse him with oddities of the language right off, with words like 'orange', where 'g' sounds 'j', or words like 'boy' where 'y' sounds 'e', or words like 'night', where two letters make no sound at all. If I did that, his logical mind would find the system illogical and he might even feel stupid.

I owed him a program that was air-tight in its logic, at least at first, so that he felt a joy in reading and never ran into exceptions to confuse his early theories. I needed a program that was at his interest level for toys and food and little songs, and I needed something that he could do for very short times a day — maybe even 10 minutes, to match his attention span.

Another top priority was a program that really taught reading. I had seen too many kids who guessed at words, reading 'commander' as 'computer' and 'devious' as 'devil'. I knew that a bad way to teach kids to read was to have them guess at words or to have them memorize little books, pretending they could read. I wanted him to actually learn to figure out what the word said, to sound it out. I realized that having him learn a lot of terms like vowel, consonant, digraph, blend, was completely unnecessary. So what was needed was something elegant and simple, with no unnecessary labels — just fun.

I did not want to push him. I wanted to take however long it took, but I wanted to move through the program step by step, so that he was gradually acquiring the alphabet and the ability to read. It became apparent that I would have to design the program myself. Maybe another existed, but I had not found it.

It really is quite simple to do this, just time-consuming. I would like to explain how other parents can do it with a few basic insights into the learning style of the very young.

At three, my son wanted to know what those marks were on the page. I figured if he could name 26 toys, that he could identify the 26 letters. But I knew I should not teach them all at once. He could not remember them all. I would have to break the task down into pieces, even as slowly as one letter every few days. For each letter I would show the shape, teach a rhyme to explain its shape, show him objects that started with the sound of the letter and show him pictures of these objects.

Initially, I decided to teach lower case letters only, to avoid confusing him. I would not require him to print the letter himself since his manual dexterity was not sophisticated enough — this would be reading only, not printing. And to further simplify it, I would make the letter's name that same sound. 'H' was huh not aitch, 'm' was muh not em. This was eminently logical since those are the sounds those letters make. I would even let him name the letter by its memory device. For instance, 'h' was also called 'house' since the memory device was that it looked like a house with a chimney.

So the first principle of the program was to simplify, simplify, simplify. Teach only one small thing at a time. The second principle was to understand his frame of reference. I entered into his world by explaining the shape of the letters in stories — 's' was a snake, 'w' was waves, m was mittens, 'c' was a curl. I entered his world by singing nursery rhymes with that sound at the start, by eating food that day that started with that sound. On the 'h' day for instance, we'd sing about Humpty Dumpty, we'd eat a hot dog, we'd look at houses and try on hats. We'd draw happy smiles on faces. We'd immerse ourselves in 'h' sounds and I'd label things around the house with that one letter, lower case 'h'.

We'd go for a walk and I'd have him feel the texture of any embossed lower-case 'h' letters we saw. I carefully ignored and did not expose him to any other letters at all, just the one we were studying or those we had studied. We did not deal with capital letters. I sorted alphabet magnets and alphabet cereal and alphabet soup letters so that I only brought to his attention the letter we were studying. Yes, it was kind of hard to set up, but my son could see what I was doing.

He could see that this was the sound of the letter, and that the letter was distinguished by its shape. It did not matter if the letter was made of cheese, or wood, or linoleum carving, or plastic, or noodles. He discriminated that what mattered about the letter was not its colour or size. He was going through the essential process of noticing relevant variables that all little kids have to deal with when they first try to read.

Often parents wonder, for instance, why a child confuses 'b' with 'd', and yet they expect the child to look at a kitchen chair, and call it a chair whether it is facing left or right. Children are very logical — they wonder if the direction of the letter matters or not, because it does not matter for labels of other objects. A child has to be taught that in this instance, direction matters. And I did this, for instance, with my poem. Every letter's shape was explained in a story I created. Lower case 'b' was 'bump on bottom': it sounded buh, and admittedly, the clue could be confused with 'd'. But for duh I gave the hint of a doorknob, and then a door. First you touch the doorknob, then you open the door. So the child got the message that if the lump at the bottom comes first, it is a doorknob duh — the letter 'd'.

Studying each letter like this was easy. It was well within the understanding of a three-year-old and each day we'd review the letter of the previous day, and some days we did no more than that. We'd cut cheese slices into that shape, roll Plasticene into that shape, and I'd even carve the shape in the sand or write it on the blackboard. We revelled in it. And then, after a few days, we'd move on and do the same with another letter.

After I had taught seven letters I added 'a', which I said was half an apple and it said ah. Then, one magic day I reviewed the eight letters we now knew, and I put two together: 'a' and 't'. I sat down with my son and showed him ah then tuh and said them together as I put them together — ah-tuh, ah-tuh, and then said it faster and faster until I was saying, "at." He probably had not a clue what I was doing. Then I did the same for three letters we'd studied — puh, ah, tuh, pat.

I put them down together from little blocks we'd made, and then I sounded them out together faster and faster until I was saying pat. I did this a few more times, with sat, sam and then quit for the day and we went to play.

The next day I showed him a few more letter blocks of the eight we knew and I showed him again how to push them together — rat, ram, pam, hat. I showed him papers with these

v

words printed next to illustrations I'd made of what they meant, and he drew a little pencil line from the word to the picture.

The next day we did a few more words with the eight letters he knew — map, mat, ram, ham. I recall vividly the first time he put the letters together and nonchalantly sounded them out. He was reading! What shocked me was that he did not seem surprised at this or anything; it was just a normal progression. He wanted to do more — and by the way, I always quit when he wanted to stop, and even sometimes made him wait until the next day if he wanted to go on a long time. In this way, reading was never a punishment and was always a game.

After our first eight letters I brought in another one, then another, and so on. Then, after a few more, we added another vowel, though I did not of course call it a vowel. Eventually I had introduced him to all 26 letters, and along the way, to any logical word combination that could be made with the ones we knew to date. I excluded all words with silent letters, double letters, or any exceptional pronunciation of letters from the restricted 26 sounds we'd studied. By the end of the alphabet, he could read at least 600 words. His self-confidence was a joy to see, and he wanted to do more.

The process took about a year. I figured it was time for the capital letters, so I invented stories of how the letters grew up — b got a new bump, h got a new chimney. I created rhymes to remind him of the sounds of the letters and logical stories about letters fighting to explain why some double letters make odd sounds. For instance, to explain long sounds of vowels in words like gate, I'd say guh wanted to talk to tuh but ah got in the way. Ah was always butting in and yelling "Get out of the way, ay," so ah now said "ay". In the situation where e got in the way, as in Pete, this little letter is bossy and keeps calling out for attention "It's me!" I invented how small i says "Hi," small oh says "Hello-o-o-o," small uh says "How are you? You-You." And the odd thing is, ridiculous as these stories seem to an adult, to a child they are logical enough, and they bridge that gap as he starts to learn a system for reading.

Armed with reasons for shapes of letters and reasons for combinations of letters making new sounds, the child had entered a kind of storyland where letters were the characters — but it was a very intriguing world to him and logical. English is one of the least logical and most difficult languages in the world, so I knew that if I really wanted to eventually have him read anything well, we'd have to move on to the exceptions and silent letters

I continued writing the program and helping him one day at a time to look at the oddities as funny too. But, as I have mentioned, we did not do this until he was very well grounded in the logic of a system that was easy to understand.

We continued until I had four volumes of books and he had now a reading vocabulary of several thousand words. Best of all, he was equipped to enter school feeling competent and excited about learning. Here is the poem the child learned, combining rhyme, rhythm, visual clues and logic for the alphabet:

huh is for house
muh is for mittens
puh pretty flower
suh snake is bitten

wuh is for waves
tuh for traintracks
ruh — round the corner
ah — apple stacks

buh — bump on bottom
cuh is for curl
duh is for doorknob
guh — long-haired girl

nuh — nail got bent
ih — it jumped up
eh — egg fell open right into a cup

oh (aw) is for octopus
uh — under umbrella
fuh has a funny top. He's a strange fella.

juh — just a jet's trail
kuh — kite on string
luh is for ladder. You climb it in spring.

vuh is for very good
yuh — yarn with tail you see
zuh is for zigzag you draw when you feel happy.

ex is for crossing the street where you've been
kwuh (q) is a lady with long dress, a queen.

My husband and I went on to have three more children, who all took this program. All four entered grade one able to read, and all did very well in school. I tutored neighbourhood kids for free, and later had people drive to my little sessions from all over the city. I am sure that other parents are anxious to ensure that their three- to five-year-olds also get a head start for school. Some of my early graduates are now in international baccalaureate programs, and faculties of law, medicine, and engineering. I must admit that I am not the only reason they are doing well. But I dare to say I played a small part. It is a real boost to children, maybe the best gift we can give next to love, to teach them to read.

Bev

Bev Jaremko

Introduction

Some Cautions and Tips

1. We are working on developing a skill, and it is a **genuine skill**. Children do not learn to read by being given magazines to look at or by being read to. These are great things to do to motivate the child, to show you love reading, to show the variety of reading available, but they won't teach the child to read. The program here is designed to give the instruction needed, but it is hoped you will also be reading to the child daily, looking at, talking about, joking about pictures and stories in your leisure time.

    I recommend that you show the child lots of kinds of books — ones with big pictures, pop-up books, washable books, ones with exciting plots and no pictures. Even just hearing the flow of English is good training for their ears, and sitting him or her on your lap to help you turn the pages makes the whole reading experience warm and a kind of bonding, too. Don't be afraid to stop and predict endings, to say what you like or dislike about the story or the artwork. Even three-year-olds have strong and wise opinions.

    In my opinion, we should not teach kids to worship books, but only to weigh their content as interesting to think about. Respecting the book by not letting the child rip it or scribble in it is important, but in our home, at least, we owned several dozen books the kids could look at in bed. Our house was strewn with garage-sale and used books and magazines. I don't think books should be stored on a shelf the child can't reach, especially if you own the books. Library books need a bit more protection, of course. If the child is keen to participate, this volume suggests ways to make pages the child can illustrate or colour.

2. The program has built-in reminders of the skills. I try to appeal to most of the five senses to show how reading relates to the child's daily life, and you can help with that. It is useful to demonstrate each new letter by printing it on a poster and putting it on the fridge, or by cutting its shape out of cheese or cardboard, or making it out of sandpaper, play-dough, or even wood. Letting the child actually feel the letter is a great teacher. Eating it works too — noodles, licorice strands.

3. The child will progress slowly. Kids vary by personality in how willing they are to actually try to read alone. You will need to help the child sound out words to demonstrate how it is done. Though a child has been taught the skills to read a word, he or she may hold back from doing this without some encouragement from you. Then suddenly, he or she will 'get it', and do it on their own. The moment varies with each child, and from what I have experienced, has nothing to do with

1

intelligence. It is more a question of who likes to hold back and be sure, and who is more outgoing and a risk-taker.

4. If the child gets confused sometimes, for instance between p and q or b and d, this is *very* normal. After all, a child who was taught to identify a chair was taught it was a chair no matter what direction it was facing. We are showing the child though, that in the case of reading, the direction a letter is facing suddenly matters. It may take time for this to become clear for the child, so be patient. The clues I give should help.

5. Printing is harder than reading for young children, who can't coordinate their hand as well as they can move their eyes. It is not really fair to ask a child to print the word just because he or she can read it. Of course, if your child wants to try, whatever he or she does, just praise them. I often had to have my kids read to me what they had printed because it was often crooked, backwards and even upside down. Until you actually are instructing the child how to print — for instance, after you've finished this book — I would suggest that you simply praise the fact that they want to be part of the process.

6. Remember that the gift you are giving the child is kind of personal. It is not intended as a skill to show off to relatives or friends. In our home we kept it as a kind of secret, in fact, to make sure not to brag about it to others. This meant that there was no emotional pressure involved.

7. The instruction method here is not quite the "See Spot run" *Phonics* method, since it does not teach formal terms, like "digraph" or "blend," or give word lists to chant out. I try to use material that the child likes to read, but like *Phonics*, this method is teaching children to sound out words.

    In some schools there is another teaching method used, called *whole language*, in which children are discouraged from sounding out words and encouraged to guess. I dislike that method because I saw the results of it in children in secondary school who did not know how to sound out new words and who would, therefore, read 'coincidence' as 'circumference'. Usually, their reading problems had by now spilled over to other courses where they were doing poorly. They rarely read anything and, sadly, also felt they were not very smart. I believe strongly that we owe children a logical system to build up their confidence in English being something they can handle in printed form. This book attempts to fill that need. Obviously, adult readers who read fast do take in big chunks of material at a time, by skimming. But beginners do not. We owe them a system at the beginning level. I believe we owe them a *Phonics*-like system, not whole language. If, however, your child is being taught by whole language, don't despair. What you do at home with this program will simply make things easier at school, whatever method is used there.

8. Some parents ask if the child who can read on entering school will be bored. The answer is that it is rarely a problem, and even if the child is bored she has an additional resource others may not have — she can read. What usually happens is the

reverse. Children feel so good about their ability that they likes school, they like the whole experience of being there, and they feels good about themselves, books, education. This confidence carries over into all their subjects, even Math.

9.   Some parents ask if a child in the **bilingual** program should learn to read English before school. As a French teacher, I must say that I am well aware that many bilingual teachers discourage English-speaking children from learning to read English before about grade three. They want them to speak French first. However, I disagree with that policy, for the simple reason that this risks creating, by about age nine, a child who is barely literate in either language. I believe that children have a natural curiosity about what those marks on the page are by between ages three and five, and it is practically cruel to deny them information in this regard. To help a child read its native tongue is part of a basic education, and I certainly would not delay it arbitrarily. What the child does outside school can be whatever you, as a parent, deem best. The school can do what it believes. I support children knowing a second language if that is the parent's preference, but I think it is an add-on, not an excuse for denying a basic skill.

10. Some will ask whether **hearing impaired** children will benefit from this material. In my experience they can certainly do it very well, if they have partial hearing. The trick is to ensure that, as with any student, the child more or less understands each page before you go on. One of the basic secrets of all good preschool education is caring about this one child's interests, moods, attention span, ensuring that he or she is looking at the paper not at the ceiling, and ensuring that praised is offered for anything he or she does well.

11. The first lesson is about pre-reading skills to make sure that the child can hold a pen or pencil and gets the idea of left-to-right progression. For level One, the child should be able to draw a line and make a sort of O around a picture. I would like to add that I don't care how the child holds the pencil. They will find a position, and will also use the hand that is comfortable.

Note to Parent: *Level One (Lessons 1–16)*

The goals of Level One of the program are as follows:

1.   At the end of Level One, the child will recognize the 26 letters, in **lower case** only. We do not use upper case because showing two shapes for one letter would confuse the child. Lower case is what most books use.

2.   The child will recognize the letters in **the font taught**. We do not yet expect the child to have to deal with various fonts, but only one basic one that is consistent throughout the book. Over time he or she will see other fonts, but to simplify the learning we stick to one basic font and match it to the visual clues. (Parents are requested also to stick to this font. It is probably the same as you would normally use, but just make sure that when you print the following letters for the child you don't add extra curls etc.)

a f g h p q r t w y z

3. The child will recognize the letters by **one sound** they make, not by their formal name. We simplify the learning a lot when we teach the letter d is duh not dee, that the letter b is buh not bee. By identifying letters by sound, we move right into the sound/letter correspondence and bypass confusion about the name. If you have already taught the child the formal alphabet names of letters, that's okay. Just downplay that for now. They are not wrong if they name the letter, but point out gently that for reading we are going to learn the sound the letter makes. It's our job to give lots of ways for the child to remember the sound when he or she sees the letter and the program is designed to do that.

4. The child will understand that reading is sounding out words from **left** to **right**.

5. The child will learn how to **attack** a new word by sounding it out, not just by guessing at it randomly.

6. The child will sound letters and words **out loud**. Children need to hear themselves say it. Don't expect silent reading yet.

7. Children will recognize the letters in their environment on signs and cereal boxes etc. but only if they are **printed large enough** to be easy to see. (Don't expect a child

to read smaller fonts yet. He or she needs to see, nice and bold, the fine details we are so concerned about, like differences between e and c as:

Note to Parent: *Level Two (Lessons 17–32)*

Level Two continues where the content of Level One left off. It taught one sound for each of the alphabet letters. Level Two introduces the proper names of these letters, the long sound of the vowels and the concept of the vowels. The capital letters, the printed digraphs sh, ch, wh, th, gh, ph, are taught, as well as the vowel digraphs ea, ai, oa, ie, where the pronunciation is the long sound of the first vowel. Variant sounds of y and one pronunciation of ar, er, or and ur are taught. We also deal with the sound of the double vowels ee and oo.

The activity approach used in Level One continues. We are using a *Phonics*-like program so that children learn to sound our words, but with lots of poems and invented stories to make the material fun and logical.

1. Reading is something you as an adult can already do. We want to make it the child's 'thing', not just your 'thing', so the mood of each five to ten minute daily session should be mostly fun. You may accomplish a page or two a day, but it is a good idea

to do more than that only at the child's insistence, not yours. This level contains more difficult material than Level One, and it is understandable and normal that the child will have a brief period of seeming confused. After all, we are now going to show him or her a second possible sound for the same letter. It is important to be patient.

2. At the end of book two the child can read thousands of words — but not all words in the language. It is still important to not make the child even try words with silent letters, words ending in -tion, words for which the strategies we taught do not work. The whole point of the approach here is to give the child success after success. We do not want to upset their growing sense of the logic of the language by presenting them with material for which they are unprepared.

3. The daily lesson is only a start, of course. Throughout the day it is useful to keep pointing out signs on the street, words in books, words on cereal boxes etc., as long as they are ones the child has been taught the skills to read. I like to print little messages to the child around the room and around the house, labelling objects, suggesting pictures to draw. Because this level also deals with capital letters, you can now greatly increase the range of store signs you can point out.

4. The letters should still be printed for the child in large script:

Children's eyes do not yet discern the fine distinctions between letters if they are printed very small.

5. The child can't really read silently yet. They have to hear themselves say the word in order to know what it says.

6. Please also keep the script style (font) the one the child has been taught. The letter shapes taught in Level One should be the ones used most of the time, and the new shapes should only be used after they are taught in Level Two. For instance

use **a** not **a**   use **g** not **g**

Lesson 1

Join the objects that are the same.

Use your pen to trace along this line. Go from left to right.

_____

_____

Use your pen to trace over these round shapes.

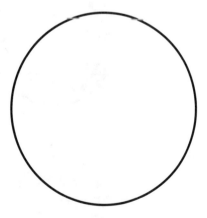

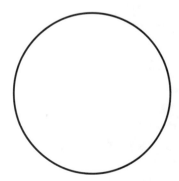

Draw a line and take the boy to the house.

Take the girl to the car.

Take the dog to the doghouse.

Here is a yard with a lot of fences. Can you find a way for the girl to walk through the yard to get to the house? She's not allowed to go over any fences, so find places with openings in the fences.

Note to Parent: Occasionally, books of very simple mazes are for sale at toy stores. You may want to try a few with your child, but remember that hard ones are frustrating.

Draw a circle around each of these pictures.

Take the boy to the house. Follow the path.

Take the girl to the park. Follow the path.

Join the dots.

Note to Parent: Dot-to-dot books are sometimes available in toystores or bookstores. Do NOT get the ones that require knowledge of numbers or letters yet, however. One should not expect the child to work with any letters or numbers until they have been taught.

13

Place a cup on this sheet and trace around it.

Trace around another toy.

Trace around one of your hands.

Note to Parent: We now start teaching the letters. The first one introduced is the letter O and is pronounced oh (as in 'open'). It is the easiest letter to identify and we teach this sound of it because it is very easy for the child to make. Later we will reintroduce the letter with the sound of o in 'octopus'. For now we call it oh.

This is the letter oh.

Notice how it looks like a donut or a ring or a plate.

Look for things in the room you are in that are shaped like O.

Sing a song you know or say a poem with the sound oh in it.

> *Roll over*
> *Old King Cole*
> *There was an old lady who swallowed a fly*
> *Oh Canada*
> *Old MacDonald had a farm*

Draw the letter oh around these faces.

Lesson 2

Sing these songs or recite the rhymes.

> *Hickory Dickory Dock*
> *Hush little baby*
> *Humpty Dumpty*
> *If you're happy and you know it*
> *Heads, shoulders, knees and toes*
> *Happy birthday*

Can you hear the sound huh in these songs?

What are these objects? Can you hear the sound huh at the start of their names?

This is how we write huh.

Circle the huhs.

o h h o

Notice how huh looks like a house with a chimney.

huh is for house

Circle the things whose names start with huh.

Circle the huhs on this page.

h

z

o

h

m

h

Join each picture to a letter huh.

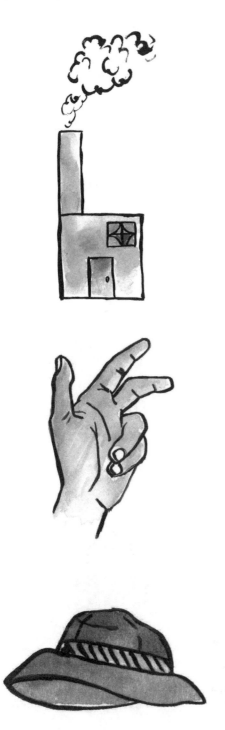

h

h

h

Feel objects that start with muh (for example, mittens, monkey, muffin, macaroni).

Sing songs or recite poems.

> *Mary had a little lamb*
> *Mary, Mary quite contrary*
> *Mulberry bush*
> *Oh Mister Sun*
> *The more we get together*

Can you hear the sound muh in these songs?

Here is how we make the letter muh.

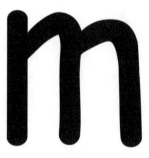

Notice how it looks like two mittens. We can call it bump-a-bump muh, mittens.

huh is for house
muh is for mittens

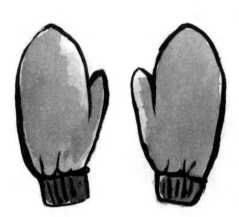

Circle the letter muhs.

h o m

m s t

m h o

Join the picture to the letter that starts its name.

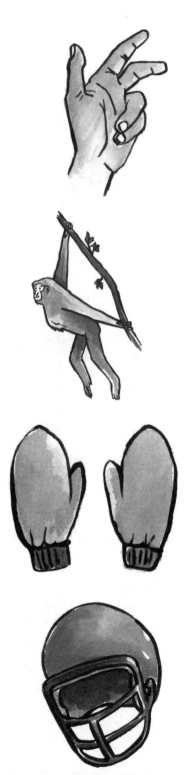

m

m

h

h

Join the picture to letter that starts its name.

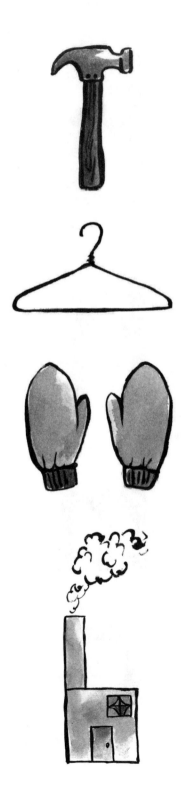

h

h

m

h

Find the letters that are the same. Draw a line from a letter on the left side to one that looks just like it on the right side.

h

m

h

o

h

h

m

o

Lesson 3

Here are some songs and poems to sing or recite.

> *Peter Piper picked a peck of pickled peppers*
> *Pease porridge hot*
> *Polly put the kettle on*
> *Pat-a-cake*
> *Pop goes the weasel*

In these poems, can you hear the letter puh?

This is how we write this letter.

It looks like a pretty flower.

Now in our poem, we have:

> *huh is for house*
> *muh is for mittens*
> *puh pretty flower*

Here is puh.

Circle the things whose names start with puh.

Circle the puhs.

p

o

p

h

p

p

m

h

Join the picture to the letter that starts its name.

p

p

m

h

Cut out these pictures and sort them in piles by their starting sound.

h m p

29

Join the letters that are the same. Draw a line from a letter on the left to one that looks just like it on the right.

h

p

m

p

p

m

p

h

31

Here are some songs and poems to try.

Simon says
Eensy weensy spider
Sing a song of sixpence
Stop, look and listen
Little Sally Saucer

Objects to feel: soap, spoon, saucer, scissors, salad.

These things have the sound ssss a lot at the start. Can you hear the suh?

This is the way we print suh.

Notice how it looks like a snake.

Poem:

huh is for house
muh is for mittens
puh pretty flower
suh — snake is bitten

Find and circle the suhs.

o s m

p h s

p s s h

Join the picture to the letter that starts its name.

h

s

m

p

34

Join the picture to the letter that starts its name.

s

h

s

h

Here is the poem so far:

> *huh is for house*
> *muh is for mittens*
> *puh pretty flower*
> *suh — snake is bitten*

Join the letters that are the same.

h

m

p

s

p

s

h

m

Lesson 4

Here are some songs and poems to try.

> *Wheels on the bus*
> *Willaby, wallaby, woo*
> *Winken, Blinken and Nod*
> *Waltzing Matilda*
> *What time is it, Mr. Wolf?*

Objects to feel: watch, wheel, water.

These things start with the sound wuh. Can you hear the wuh?

This is how we print wuh.

It looks like waves on the water.

Poem:

> *huh is for house*
> *muh is for mittens*
> *puh pretty flower*
> *suh — snake is bitten*
> *wuh is for waves*

37

We have now learned two letters that look a little bit alike. Here they are. What are they?

Do you see the difference? wuh has points on the bottom, like waves. muh has bumps on the top.

Find the wuhs below and circle them.

w   m   w

h   w   p

m   p   w

Join the letters that are the same.

w

m

m

s

h

p

p

w

s

h

Join the letter to a picture that starts with that sound.

w

m

w

m

Join the picture to the letter that starts its name.

h

p

s

w

Here are some songs and poems to try.

> *Twinkle twinkle little star*
> *Little Tommy Tucker*
> *Ten little Indians*
> *I'm a little teapot*

Objects to feel: table, twig, tooth, toe.

These things start with the sound tuh.
Can you hear the sound tuh at the start of those words?

This is the way we print the sound tuh.

Notice how it looks like train tracks.

Here's our poem now:

> *huh is for house*
> *muh is for mittens*
> *puh pretty flower*
> *suh — snake is bitten*
> *wuh is for waves*
> *tuh for train tracks*

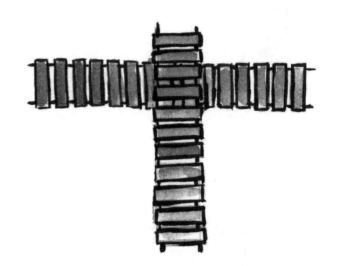

Circle the things that start with tuh.

Find and circle the puhs.

p h p t

Find and circle the tuhs.

t s m t

Find and circle the wuhs.

w m t p

Find and circle the suhs.

w s o p

Join the picture to the letter that starts its name.

Lesson 5

Songs and poems to try.

Rub a dub dub
Roll over
Rock-a-bye baby
Row, row, row your boat
Rudolph the red-nosed reindeer

Objects to feel: ring, rug, radish, rock.

Can you hear the sound ruh in these words?
Here is the way we print the sound ruh.

It looks like the path as you run around a corner.

Poem so far (read to the child down one column, then down the next):

huh is for house   *wuh is for waves*
muh is for mittens   *tuh for traintracks*
puh — pretty flower   *ruh — round the corner*
suh — snake is bitten

Join the picture to the letter that starts its name.

r

t

r

h

Circle the ruhs.

r t r s

Circle the muhs.

m w r m

Circle the suhs.

t s o s

Circle the tuhs.

r t r t

Join the picture to the letter that starts its name.

w

m

p

r

What are these things?

They all start with the sound ah.

Here are some songs and poems with that sound.

> Ants go marching
> Away in a manger
> Animal fair
> Alouette

Here is the way we print the sound ah.
(Parent, please say ah as in 'ant', not as in 'awful' or 'age'.)

Ah looks like an apple that got stacked up in piles and then partly eaten.

Poem so far (again, read down one column, then down the next):

> huh is for house   wuh is for waves
> muh is for mittens   tuh for traintracks
> puh — pretty flower   ruh round the corner
> suh — snake is bitten ah — apple stacks

Circle the things that start with ah.

51

Now we can put together some of the letters we know.

Try putting these sounds together.

Note to Parent: You will have to slowly demonstrate the combination of the sounds. The child will not understand them.

at   am

Now try some words. When you've read each sound, say them all together along the line and you'll have the word. To show what the word means, join the word to the picture it names.

hat

pat

mat

52

Now join these words to their pictures.

ham

mama

sam

Note to Parent: The sound in 'mama' is a slight variation of the sound in 'ham'. It usually does not confuse the child.

Match the letter on the left side with the one just like it on the right side.

W

t

r

a

s

t

r

a

w

s

Here are some labels to read and cut out. You can tape them up around your house near the thing they name.

mat   hat

tap   mama

papa

Lesson 6

Try to remember our poem and join the pictures to the letters that match — huh is for house, muh is for mittens and so on.

m

p

h

s

Now join these pictures to the letters they start with.

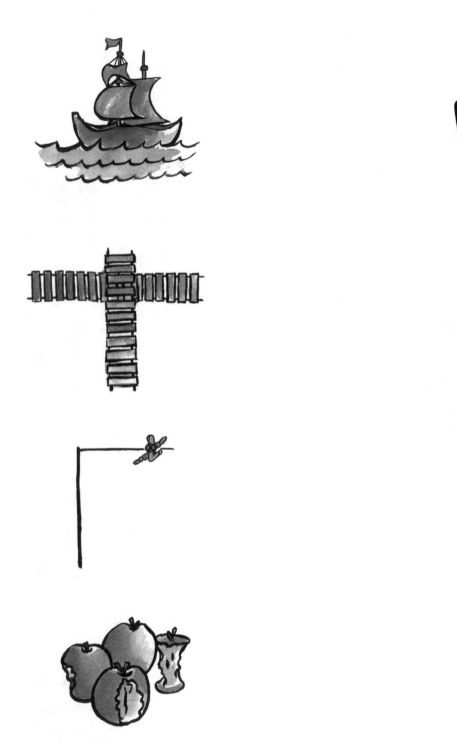

w

r

t

a

Join these pictures to the words that name them.

rat

mat

pat

Join these pictures to the words that name them.

ram

tap

sam

On the left are some of the letters we learned. In each row look for the letter that is the same as the one at the left and draw a circle around it. The first set is done for you.

Example.

h | o (h) s

Now you try.

s | c o s

r | i r w

t | t r v

a | o c a

Lesson 7

Name these objects.

Do you notice how they start with the sound buh?

Here are some songs and poems that have this sound in them.

> Baa baa black sheep
> Bye-bye baby bunting
> Bingo
> Boom boom made the great to be...crazy

Other objects to feel that start with buh: bone, banana, bread, box, balloon, bat, bag.

This is a buh. Notice how it looks like a line with a bump on the bottom.

Here is our poem so far:

huh is for house   wuh is for waves   buh — bump on bottom
muh is for mittens   tuh for traintracks
puh — pretty flower   ruh round the corner
suh — snake is bitten ah — apple stacks

Circle the things that start with buh.

Find in each row a letter like the one on the left and circle it.

b | c o **b**

a | c s **a**

m | **m** w h

h | n **h** m

Join the picture to the letter that starts its name.

m

b

w

h

Name these objects.

Here are more songs and poems.

Camptown races   O come all ye faithful
Clementine   Five currant buns
The cat came back

Notice how these things have words with the sound cuh in them.

Here is how we print the letter cuh.

C

Notice how it looks like a curl on a girl's hair.

Here is our poem so far:

huh is for house   wuh is for waves   buh — bump on bottom
muh is for mittens   tuh for traintracks   cuh is for curl
puh — pretty flower   ruh — round the corner
suh — snake is bitten   ah — apple stacks

Join the picture to the letter that starts its name.

b

c

a

c

Join the picture to the letter that starts its name.

c

b

r

t

Join the picture to the letter that starts its name.

b

c

t

w

69

Now say each sound in the word and then put the sounds along the line together and make a word. Then join the word to the picture it matches.

bat

cat

rat

Lesson 8

What are these things?

Here are some songs and poems with the new sound.

Davy Crockett　　　　　*Down by the farm*　　　*Ding, dong, merrily on high*
Little white duck

Do you hear the sound duh in these words? This is how we print the sound duh.

Notice how it looks like a doorknob that you reach for when you want to open a door.

Do you remember another letter that we learned that was a line with a bump? It was buh.

Can you see a difference between them?

　　　buh　　　　　　　　　　duh

Now, how can you remember buh and duh and not mix them up?

You could think of buh as a bump on bottom, but first you have to draw the thing that has the bottom. First the line, then the bump.

For duh, you could remember that you reach for the doorknob, and then you open the door.

Everybody mixes up buh and duh at first. But you can remember if you think of our poem.

Another way to remember is to think of a bed. The first sound is buh and that makes the line of the bed and then the bump. And the last sound is duh, and that ends the bed so the line is at the back.

Here is our poem so far:

huh is for house	*wuh is for waves*	*buh bump on bottom*
muh is for mittens	*tuh for traintracks*	*cuh is for curl*
puh — pretty flower	*ruh — round the corner*	*duh is for doorknob*
suh — snake is bitten	*ah — apple stacks*	

Circle the duhs below.

b c d d

Now join the letters that are the same.

b

c

d

o

b

b

d

b

o

c

73

Join the picture to the letter that starts its name.

a

r

d

c

What are these things?

Do you hear the sound guh at the start of these words?

Here are some other objects to touch — things that start with guh: grape, ground, gold, glass.

Here is how we print the sound guh.

Notice how it looks like a girl with long hair.

Here is our poem now:

huh is for house	*wuh is for waves*	*buh — bump on bottom*
muh is for mittens	*tuh for traintracks*	*cuh is for curl*
puh — pretty flower	*ruh — round the corner*	*duh is for doorknob*
suh — snake is bitten	*ah — apple stacks*	*guh — long-haired girl*

Join the picture to the letter that starts its name.

g

d

g

b

Join the picture to the letter that starts its name.

w

r

g

p

Join the picture to the letter that starts its name.

g

d

c

a

Now sound out these letters and then put them together to see what word they make. Then join the word to its picture.

bag

sad

hat

Join the picture hint to the letter we use in our poem.

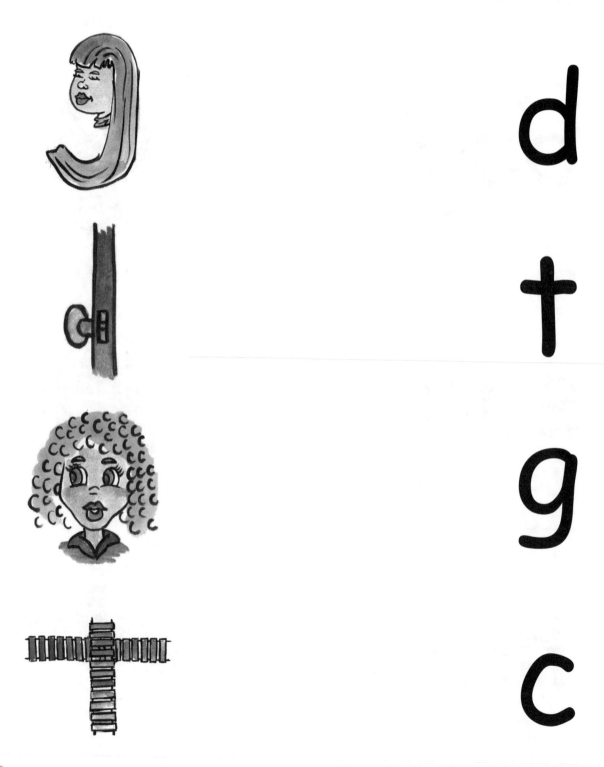

d

t

g

c

Lesson 9

What are these objects?

Can you hear the sound nuh at the start of these words?

Here are some songs and poems with this sound.

> *Nobody likes me* *The first Noel*
> *Silent night* *Winken, Blinken and Nod*

Objects to feel: nose, neck, nuts, nail (fingernail).

Here is the way we print the sound nuh.

Notice how it looks like a nail that got bent.

We already learned two other letters that have bumps. Do you remember huh and muh?

Can you see a difference between them all?

huh muh nuh

81

For huh, we remember a house.

For muh, we remember mittens — bump-a-bump

For nuh, we have a nail that got bent.
It has one bump, not two bumps.

Here is our poem now:

huh is for house   *ruh — round the corner*   *nuh — nail got bent*
muh is for mittens   *ah — apple stacks*
puh — pretty flower   *buh — bump on bottom*
suh — snake is bitten *cuh is for curl*
wuh is for waves   *duh is for doorknob*
tuh for traintracks   *guh — long-haired girl*

Circle the things that start with nuh.

Join each letter on the left with a letter on the right that is the same.

n

m

h

r

t

r

n

h

t

m

83

Sound out these letters on each line to make a word.
Then join the word to the picture that matches.

cap

nap

gas

pan

What are these objects?

These things start with the sound ih. (Parent, say ih as in 'it' not as in 'ice' or 'I'.)

Here are some songs and poems with this sound:

> In and out the window   If you're happy
> In a cottage in a wood   Itsy bitsy spider

The sound ih is printed like this.

Notice how it looks like a very little line and it jumped up.
It has a dot on top from jumping.

Here is our poem now:

> huh is for house   ruh — round the corner   nuh — nail got bent
> muh is for mittens   ah — apple stacks   ih — it jumped up
> puh — pretty flower   buh — bump on bottom
> suh — snake is bitten   cuh is for curl
> wuh is for waves   duh is for doorknob
> tuh for traintracks   guh — long-haired girl

Look at the letter on the left side and circle the one on the right that is the same.

i | l r i

n | r n m

t | n l t

g | p d g

Join the words that are the same. You will have to sound out each letter, and it's a little tricky, so watch out!

in   pin

it   is

is   it

pin   in

Join these words to the pictures that match them.

pig

dig

mitt

sit

Join the picture to the letter that starts its name.

n

p

g

i

Join these words to the pictures that match them.

tin

pin

pan

sit

Lesson 10

Join the letters that are the same.

o

h

m

p

w

h

m

w

o

p

91

Look at the letter on the left and find and circle the one on the right that is the same.

t	r t i
r	n r h
a	o c a
b	d g b
c	c o s

Here are some words to cut out and paste up around the house.

hat

tin

bag

mitt

pan

sit

pin

Sound out these words and join them to the pictures they match.

tin

wig

big

pan

Lesson 11

What are these things?

Do you hear the sound eh at the start of these words?
(Parent, say eh as in 'egg' not as in 'eat'.)

Here are some songs and poems with the sound.

> Everyone clap hands like me
> The elephant

You can feel an **empty** box or the **end** of a pencil.
Do you hear the sounds eh in these words?

Here is how we make eh.

Notice how it looks like an egg that cracked and fell open. Maybe people were picking it up and when it broke they took one part of it and put it in a cup.

Here is our poem now:

huh is for house	ruh — round the corner	nuh — nail got bent
muh is for mittens	ah — apple stacks	ih — it jumped up
puh — pretty flower	buh — bump on bottom	eh — egg fell open
suh — snake is bitten	cuh is for curl	right into a cup
wuh is for waves	duh is for doorknob	
tuh for traintracks	guh — long-haired girl	

Find the ehs and circle them.

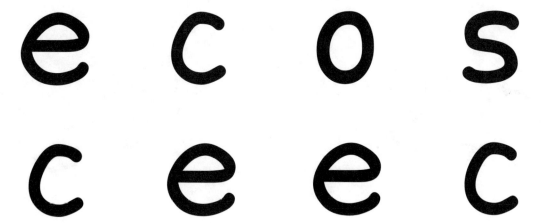

e c o s

c e e c

Circle the things that start with the sound eh.

Sound out these words and join them to their pictures.

egg

bed

hen

net

Sound out these words and join them to their pictures.

sad

pen

pet

wet

net

What are these things? (olive/octopus)

Do you notice how they start with the sound aw? (Parent, pronounce it oh as in 'pot'.)

Here are some songs with that sound.

> On top of old Smokey
> Come on and join into the game
> We're off to see the Wizard

Here is how we print the sound aw.

O

Remember a long time ago we learned the letter oh (as in oh). It is a circle, isn't it? Well, this is the same letter.

This letter can have two sounds. One is oh, and the other is aw, but usually it says aw. When we see it, let's remember an octopus and say aw.

Here is our poem now:

huh is for house	buh bump on bottom	oh (aw) is for octopus
muh is for mittens	cuh is for curl	
puh pretty flower	duh is for doorknob	
suh snake is bitten	guh — long-haired girl	
wuh is for waves	nuh — nail got bent	
tuh for traintracks	ih — it jumped up	
ruh — round the corner	eh — egg fell open	
ah — apple stacks	right into a cup	

Join the letters that are the same.

o

e

c

a

s

g

e

a

s

o

g

c

Sound out these words and join them to the pictures that match.

dog

pot

hog

ron

Sound out these words and join them to the pictures that match.

pin

pig

pan

cat

Join the letters that match.

h

n

m

t

r

n

h

m

r

t

Sound out these words and join them to pictures that match.

cat

pig

dog

net

Note to Parent: Here is a partial list of words the child now can sound out. You may want to reprint these larger and put them around the house. Make sure when you print them you use the print style the child has learned. To use a different one would confuse the child right now. Do not expect the child to be able to read all of these. A few will do.

g should be like this g not this g
a should be like this a not this a

hat	ham	had	tab	pep	rag
mat	pam	bin	mad	cab	bag
wet	ron	pat	sam	pad	peg
dab	swept	don	sat	rat	beg
hit	pit	mitt	sit	bit	pig
met	pet	set	wet	bet	wig
get	net	hot	pot	tot	big
rot	cot	dot	got	not	dig
ram	dam	him	tim	rim	hog
dim	mom	tom	mass	gas	dog
pass	sis	mess	west	tad	cat
best	rest	toss	boss	bad	rat
dad	wed	ted	red	bed	spend
ned	hid	sid	bid	did	end
pod	rod	cod	nod	pod	bend
deb	rib	bib	mob	sob	send
rob	bob	hip	sip	tip	snap
rip	dip	map	sap	tap	cap
cap	gap	nap	hop	mop	tap
pop	stop	crop	top	hen	rap
men	pen	ten	ben	den	rip
man	pan	ran	can	dan	brat
pin	win	tin	wag	tag	sat

Lesson 12

What is this object?

An umbrella starts with the sound uh. (Parent, say uh as in 'under'.)

Here are some songs and poems with that sound.

> *My hand upon my head*   *It came upon a midnight clear*
> *Up, up and away*

Can you hear the sound uh? This sound is written like this.

Notice how it looks like the path of someone walking under something.
It's as if someone is lying under two tall umbrellas.

We already learned a letter that looks like uh only upside down. Do you remember nuh?

Can you see the difference between nuh and uh?

107

Find and circle the uhs.

u u n o u

Here's our poem so far:

huh is for house	*buh bump on bottom*	*oh (aw) is for octopus*
muh is for mittens	*cuh is for curl*	*uh — under umbrella*
puh — pretty flower	*duh is for doorknob*	
suh — snake is bitten	*guh — long-haired girl*	
wuh is for waves	*nuh — nail got bent*	
tuh for traintracks	*ih — it jumped up*	
ruh — round the corner	*eh — egg fell open*	
ah — apple stacks	*right into a cup*	

Now look at the letter at the left and find the one at the right that is the same and circle it.

u	w	n	u
n	h	n	o
h	h	m	n
e	c	e	s

Sound out these words and join them to their pictures.

gum

pup

bun

wig

Sound out these words and join them to their pictures.

bug

nuts

net

bag

What are these things?

These things start with the sound fuh.

Here are some songs and poems with that sound.

Fuzzy wuzzy   *First Noel*
10 little fingers   *Frere Jacques*
Farmer in the dell   *Put your finger in the air*
There came a girl from France

Here are some things whose names start with fuh.
Try to find them around your house: finger, fuzz, fur, feather, fan, foot.

The sound fuh is printed like this.

See how it looks like another letter we learned — tuh — except that it has a funny top.

Can you see the difference?

So fuh is just tuh with a funny top.
Circle the fuhs below.

111

Here is our poem now:

huh is for house   buh — bump on bottom   oh (aw) is for octopus
muh is for mittens   cuh is for curl   uh — under umbrella
puh — pretty flower   duh is for doorknob   fuh has a funny top.
suh — snake is bitten   guh — long-haired girl   He's a strange fella.
wuh is for waves   nuh — nail got bent
tuh for traintracks   ih — it jumped up
ruh — round the corner   eh — egg fell open
ah — apple stacks   right into a cup

Circle the things that start with fuh.

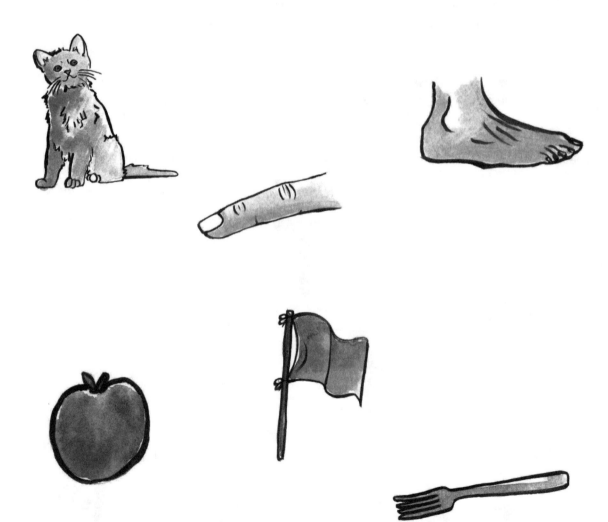

Here are some words to read aloud and cut out and paste around the house.

fan rug

crib pens

cups sit

drip bags

bed

Sound out these words and join them to the pictures they match.

cup

cross

cut

drip

115

Sound out these words and join them to the pictures they match.

cabin

fan

crib

grass

Here is a list of some more words the child can now read. There are also a few phrases he or she can sound out. You could reprint these larger and paste them around the house, or you might want to ask the child to draw a picture of what they mean, or to act out a few. Don't do them all, a few will do.

Note to Parent: In the word 'pets', the letter suh says ssss. In the word 'has', the letter suh says zzzz. If the child notices this, just say that suh sometimes makes a zz sound. If the child does not seem to notice or does not seem bothered by this, there is no need to point it out to him/her.

hum	hug	gum	up	cup	bus
gus	hut	mutt	but	cut	tub
rub	cub	sun	run	bun	gun
nun	fun	hug	mug	tug	rug
bug	dug	mud	puff	huff	rust

rub a dub dub	men in a tub
dan is in	it's pam
dog bit him	pig naps
dan sent a hot dog	rip the cap
bent the pen	ron pets his dog
his mitt is big	a magnet
spots on his cat	hand in a bag
egg on a mat	swim in a tub
ten mittens	is dad sad
dad is mad	ten pigs in a pen
ten cats in a bag	tim gets wet
pat has a wig	meg has a pig
dan has a cat	pam has a bib
sam had a pan	is a rat bad
can meg add	

117

Lesson 13

What are these objects? These words start with the sound juh.

Here are some songs and poems with that sound.

Jack and Jill   *John Henry*
Jack Sprat   *Jack be nimble*
Jingle bells   *Jacob's ladder*
Joy to the world

Can you hear the sound juh in these songs and poems? Here is how we print the sound juh.

Do you notice how it looks a lot like another letter we learned — ih (as in 'pit')?

Well, both of them have a dot on the top, don't they? Can you see any difference between them?

i j

Juh looks like ih except it had just a little curl and then it jumped up. It looks a little like a jet airplane that took off from the airport and went up high, leaving a trail.

Here is our poem now:

huh is for house
muh is for mittens
puh — pretty flower
suh — snake is bitten
wuh is for waves
tuh for traintracks
ruh — round the corner
ah — apple stacks

buh — bump on bottom
cuh is for curl
duh is for doorknob
guh — long-haired girl
nuh — nail got bent
ih — it jumped up
eg — egg fell open
    right into a cup

oh (aw) is for octopus
uh — under umbrella
fuh has a funny top.
    He's a strange fella.
juh — just a jet's trail

Find the juhs and circle them.

Join these pictures to the letter that starts their name.

119

Look at the letter on the left, and find the one on the right just like it and circle it.

j	f	j	c
f	t	f	r
u	n	h	u
d	p	d	b
t	r	t	f

Sound out these words and join them to the picture that matches.

jet

jam

jug

jim

121

What are these objects?

These things start with the sound kuh.

Here are some songs and poems with this sound.

> *Kookaburra*
> *Kumbaya*
> *Keep the Home Fires Burning*

Do you hear the sound kuh in these words? Now, we already know a letter that makes the sound cuh, don't we?

Well here is another letter that makes the same sound. Here is how it looks.

k

Notice how it looks like three sticks, or two sticks with one bent. When you see it, you could think of a boy standing still but holding a kite up and a string going down.

Find and circle the kuhs.

h k t k

Here is our poem now:

huh is for house
muh is for mittens
puh — pretty flower
suh — snake is bitten
wuh is for waves
tuh for traintracks
ruh — round the corner
ah — apple stacks

buh — bump on bottom
cuh is for curl
duh is for doorknob
guh — long-haired girl
nuh — nail got bent
ih — it jumped up
eg — egg fell open
   right into a cup

oh (aw) is for octopus
uh under umbrella
fuh has a funny top.
   He's a strange fella.
juh — just a jet's trail
kuh — kite on string

Circle the things that start with the sound kuh.

Sound out these words and join them to the pictures that they match.

kiss

kitten

kid

kit

Look at the letter on the left and then look at the pictures on the right. Find a picture of something that starts with the sound on the left in each row and circle that picture.

Circle the picture whose name starts with the sound on the left.

f

e

g

r

i

s

Here are some signs that you may see in the streets. Try to read the ones with letters and talk about what you think the others mean.

Lesson 14

What are these objects?

Do you hear the sound luh in these words?

Here are some songs and poems that also have the sound luh.

Little Bo Peep   *Looby loo*
London Bridge   *Little white duck*
Lullaby and good-night   *Lou, lou skip to my lou*

Here is how we print the sound luh.

Notice how it is just a straight line,
all alone. It looks like a ladder.

Here is our poem now:

huh is for house
muh is for mittens
puh — pretty flower
suh — snake is bitten
wuh is for waves
tuh for traintracks
ruh — round the corner
ah — apple stacks

buh — bump on bottom
cuh is for curl
duh is for doorknob
guh — long-haired girl
nuh — nail got bent
ih — it jumped up
eg — egg fell open
　　right into a cup

oh (aw) is for octopus
uh — under umbrella
fuh has a funny top.
　　He's a strange fella.
juh — just a jet's trail
kuh — kite on string
luh is for ladder.
　　You climb it in spring.

Look at the pictures below and join the picture hint to the letter it matches.

129

Join these words to their pictures.

lips

log

hill

pals

Join these words to their pictures.

pill

lid

lap

fill

What are these objects?

Do you hear the sound vuh at the start of these words?

Here are some songs and poems with this sound.

Viva la Compagnie   *Volare*

Here is how we print the sound vuh.

If you were eating cake and it was very good, you might want another piece of it. You could hold up two fingers to show you wanted two pieces.

The letter vuh makes you think of 'very good'. If the teacher at school thinks your work is very good, he or she might make a mark on your page like this, which is sort of like vuh.

Sometimes when people are happy they hold up their fingers to make a vuh to remember the word victory, which means winning.

We already know some letters that look a little like vuh. Can you see the differences?

wuh   nuh   vuh

Our poem is getting very long now. Here it is. See if you can remember it as it is read.

huh is for house
muh is for mittens
puh pretty flower
suh — snake is bitten
wuh is for waves
tuh for traintracks
ruh — round the corner
ah — apple stacks

buh — bump on bottom
cuh is for curl
duh is for doorknob
guh — long-haired girl
nuh — nail got bent
ih — it jumped up
eh — egg fell open
   right into a cup

oh (aw) is for octopus
uh — under umbrella
fuh has a funny top.
   He's a strange fella.
juh — just a jet's trail
kuh — kite on string
luh is for ladder.
   You climb it in spring.
vuh is for very good

Now look at the letter on the left, and find the one on the right that's the same and circle it.

v	v o w l
l	r l k u
f	t f v j
u	w u r v
j	p i j f

133

Sound out these words and join them to the pictures they match.

van

vest

vet

kevin

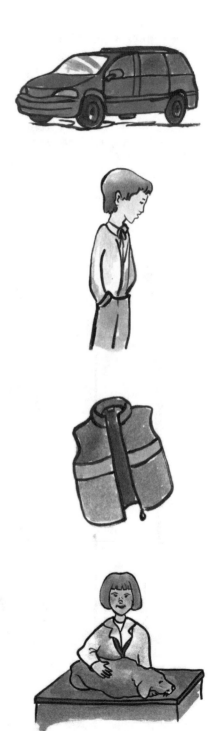

Join the letters that are the same.

r

r

n

g

v

k

l

v

k

n

g

l

135

Here are some more words to print larger and to stick around the house.

Note to Parent: Make sure again you use the print style that the child has learned. e.g., a and g not a and g

jam	jack	jan	jet	jim
deck	jog	job	just	jug
keg	kim	kiss	kit	kid
pack	sack	tack	rack	back
pick	neck	sick	wick	tick
dick	kick	lick	sock	rock
clock	rick	buck	duck	plan
lock	puck	suck	tuck	vet
luck	clam	clap	class	jot
plan	bliss	flap	flip	ken
black	blink	block	bled	kill
flop	flat	flag	fun	flick
flock	vest	vent	van	

jack and jill went up a hill
ken had a sick dog
rick has black socks
his duck is well
tom hit bob and bob fell
his cat is sad
a big duck bit him
ten hats fell on jim

Lesson 15

Here are some questions your parent will read to you. See if you can answer them.

Does a dog have four legs? _____

What colour is the sun? _____

What is that long stringy stuff people use to knit with? _____

The answers to these questions start with the sound yuh.

Here are some songs and poems that use this sound.

Yankee Doodle   *You are my sunshine*
If you're happy and you know it

Here is how we print the sound yuh.

Notice how it looks a little like another letter we learned, vuh. What is the difference between them?

yuh    vuh

Yuh is like vuh only it has a tail and you can see the tail.

Another way to remember it is to think of lots of yarn with two knitting needles sticking out.

137

Circle the yuhs (look for the tail).

Here is our poem so far:

huh is for house
muh is for mittens
puh — pretty flower
suh — snake is bitten
wuh is for waves
tuh for traintracks
ruh — round the corner
ah — apple stacks
buh — bump on bottom
cuh is for curl

duh is for doorknob
guh — long-haired girl
nuh — nail got bent
ih — it jumped up
eh — egg fell open
    right into a cup
oh (aw) is for octopus
uh — under umbrella
fuh has a funny top.
    He's a strange fella.

juh — just a jet's trail
kuh — kite on string
luh is for ladder.
    You climb it in spring.
vuh is for very good
yuh — yarn with tail you see

Join the letters that are the same.

Sound out these words and join them to their pictures.

yell

yak

cat

dog

Here are some more questions to answer when your parent read them.

What is the place you visit where animals
are kept in cages? _____

What is the big animal that looks like a horse
but has black and white stripes? _____

Some coats do up because they have buttons.
What's another way they do up? _____

The answers to these questions use words that start with zuh ('zoo', 'zebra', 'zipper').

Here is how we print the sound zuh.

This looks like a zigzag drawing where your pencil just goes back and forth down the page.

Try to draw a zigzag on this page yourself.

Here are some other letters. Circle the zuh.

z n s r

Now, guess what? We're going to add one more part to our poem and it's nearly done!

Can you remember it so far?

huh is for house
muh is for mittens
puh — pretty flower
suh — snake is bitten
wuh is for waves
tuh for train tracks
ruh — round the corner
ah — apple stacks
buh — bump on bottom
cuh is for curl

duh is for doorknob
guh — long-haired girl
nuh — nail got bent
ih — it jumped up
eg — egg fell open
    right into a cup
oh (aw) is for octopus
uh — under umbrella
fuh has a funny top.
    He's a strange fella.

juh — just a jet's trail
kuh — kite on string
luh is for ladder.
    You climb it in spring.
vuh is for very good
yuh — yarn with tail you see
zuh is for zigzag
    — you draw when you
    feel happy

Join the letters to their hints from the poem.

Join the letters that are the same.

z

n

v

r

w

y

r

w

y

v

n

z

Here are some more labels to paste up around your house.

glass

doll

desk

lamp

socks

rug

step

hat

truck

bulb

Join the picture to the letter that starts its name.

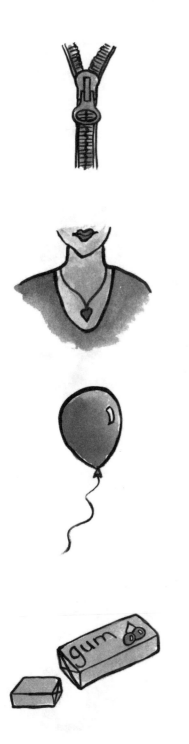

Look at the letter on the left and find the one on the right that is the same and circle it.

d | b p **d**

v | r v w

y | v w **y**

f | **f** t j

s | c **s** a

Lesson 16

Here are some questions to answer.

When a doctor takes pictures of your insides,
what are the pictures called? _____

The door to go in is the entrance.
What is the name of the door to go out? _____

How do you feel the day before your
birthday? (excited) _____

These words have the sound ex in them.

Here is how we print ex.

If you are walking down the street you come to a corner and you see another street. The streets meet at the corner and we say they cross. They look like the letter ex don't they?

If you are coming to a railway, the place where the tracks cross the road sometimes has a sign that is an ex too. It means a railway is crossing the road.

If you put your hands together you can make one finger cross over the other to make an ex. Try it.

Here is our poem now:

huh is for house
muh is for mittens
puh — pretty flower
suh — snake is bitten
wuh is for waves
tuh for traintracks
ruh — round the corner
ah — apple stacks
buh — bump on bottom
cuh is for curl

duh is for doorknob
guh — long-haired girl
nuh — nail got bent
ih — it jumped up
eh — egg fell open
    right into a cup
oh (aw) is for octopus
uh — under umbrella
fuh has a funny top.
    He's a strange fella.

juh — just a jet's trail
kuh — kite on string
luh is for ladder.
    You climb it in spring.
vuh is for very good
yuh — yarn with tail you see
zuh is for zigzag
    you draw when you are
    happy
ex is for crossing the street
    where you've been

Now ex looks a little like another letter that we learned — tuh. Can you see a difference?

Circle the exs.

r x n x t

Sound out these words and join them to their pictures.

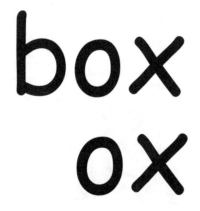

Join the letters that are the same.

x

k

t

t

x

k

Sound out these words and join them to their pictures.

fox

boxes

Here are some sentences to finish.

> The king's wife is called the _____.

> A coin that is worth 25 cents is
> also called a _____.

> You sometimes ask "Why?" Somebody answers.
> What you are asking is called a _____.

The words we are talking about contain the sound kwuh. (Parent, don't say cue.)

Here are some songs and poems that have this sound.

> *Six little ducks, quack quack quack*
> *The quartermaster's store*
> *God save the Queen*

Here is how we print the sound kwuh.

Notice how it looks like a queen with a long dress and cape.

We already learned some other letters that look a little like kwuh. Can you see the difference? Kwuh (q) is the first one in the row.

q g p b d

Now, this is getting tricky. All those letters have lines and circles. What's the difference?

guh is a girl with long hair.

g

puh is pretty flower.

p

buh is bump on bottom.

b

duh is for doorknob.
Remember the doorknob, then the door.

d

And the new letter,
kwuh, is a queen with a long straight dress.

q

Circle the kwuhs.

g q q b d

151

Join the letters that are the same.

g

p

q

g

p

b

b

q

Do you remember how we sometimes wondered if a letter was buh or duh, and we thought of a bed?

Well if you sometimes wonder if a letter is puh or kwuh, here is a trick.

Think of a pretty girl looking at a quiet boy...

Sound out these words and join them to their pictures.

pup

bun

jam

gum

drum

Sound out these words and join them to the pictures that match.

tracks

wagon

hand

umbrella

Here is our poem, at last!

huh is for house
muh is for mittens
puh pretty flower
suh snake is bitten
wuh is for waves
tuh for train tracks
ruh — round the corner
ah — apple stacks

buh — bump on bottom
cuh is for curl
duh is for doorknob
guh — long-haired girl

nuh — nail got bent
ih — it jumped up
eh — egg fell open right into a cup

oh (aw) is for octopus
uh under umbrella
fuh has a funny top. He's a strange fella.

juh — just a jet's trail
kuh — kite on string
luh is for ladder. You climb it in spring.

vuh is for very good
yuh — yarn with tail you see
zuh is for zigzag — You draw when you feel happy

ex is for crossing the street where you've been
kwuh (q) is a lady with long dress, a queen.

Now you know all the letters! **Congratulations!**

Sound out these words and join them to the pictures that match.

duck

bus

bug

grass

You have now learned every letter that is in English. You can practise the poem to help you remember them all. And you can sound out hundreds of words!

Note to Parent: What your child can do:

1. Identify each of the 26 letters of the alphabet by ONE sound it makes (not its name).

2. Know the short sound of the five vowels.

3. Read words that are in lower case, printed very large, in the one font we taught.

4. Sound out any word in English that follows the above rules (any word that does not have long vowels, silent letters, or variant sounds like ing, sh, ch, ph, th, gh, or variant sounds of vowels not taught — e.g., aw in car).

What your child cannot do:

1. She cannot be perfect. She will make lots of mistakes. Be encouraging and patient.

2. She cannot sit down and read a book yet, but she can enjoy sounding out occasional words in books you read together.

3. She may be reluctant to try to read on her own, even though you know that she can do it. She needs encouragement letter by letter pointing and asking "What's that?", to help reinforce the idea of putting the sounds together.

Things you can do from here:

1. Praise her a lot for learning the letters.

2. Point out lower case letters in stores, on packages, on street signs, casually and occasionally. Make sure you are only pointing out lower case letters and ones large enough for the child to read. Only point out ones in the font taught (ɡ not g, ɑ not a).

3. Review the pages you've done if the child wants to.

4. Read aloud to the child daily, and read your own books and papers in front of her sometimes as she plays.

5. Go on to Level Two of this program, which teaches the upper case letters, the names of the letters formally, variant sounds of sh, ch, ph, th and the long vowel sounds. This will take the reading vocabulary of your child to the thousands.

6. Congratulate yourself. You have invested well in your child's future. You have opened up a new world to her, and the printed page will never be just a mass of marks again.

Here is another partial list of words the child can now sound out. You can reprint them larger and paste them around the house. You can have the child read a few and draw pictures to match them. You could even have the child help you make a little picture dictionary with some of them.

allan	alan	alfred	alvin	angus	benjamin
conrad	dennis	derek	edmund	eric	frank
grant	jack	kent	patrick	rex	ross
scott	todd	wendell	ann	anna	belinda
brenda	cassandra	edna	ellen	erica	estella
helen	hilda	ingrid	jessica	jill	linda
melissa	monica	miranda	pamela	robin	roxanna
sara	bev	hat	mittens	socks	top
pants	dress	slip	umbrella	big	hot
dull	fun	red	pink	fat	bed
lamp	desk	pen	pot	pan	cup
mug	stop	exit	on	off	is
unless	until	cat	dog	duck	pig
hog	past	until	ten	six	seven
canada	winnipeg	halifax	west	job	bank
boss	spell	nap	rest	address	print
class	sex	montana	texas	atlantic	pakistan
japan	dallas	attack	back	baptist	basket
credit	lift	batman	bedpan	black	red
blast	bless	bonnet	boss	box	brag
brand	ink	buck	bug	bum	bump
bun	bus	button	buzz	cabin	camp
campus	canal	cannon	canvas	crab	crib
cap	cast	clip	clink	club	cluck
cobweb	cockpit	cod	compliment	complex	coffin
contest	cost	cramp	critic	crust	cross
cutlet	deck	dust	den	dig	dip
dim	connect	disconnect	dismiss	distress	dock
drip	drop	drug	drunk	dump	edit
elf	emblem	exam	test	express	fast
fact	fan	fell	fist	film	fin
flapjack	fond	fragment	frill	fuss	gal
gap	gas	gut	grunt	grass	get
gig	glad	glob	got	grad	grin
grand	grill	grip	had	habit	ham
hansel	gretel	help	hem	hen	hexagon
him	hip	hiss	goblin	holland	hop
hunt	hut	ill	insist	invest	jump
junk	just	kilt	kit	kept	land
lamp	list	let	lap	leg	lisp

lick	lift	lint	lid	luck	log
lock	lost	lump	mast	magnet	map
medal	met	mend	mess	miss	print
model	miss	must	muffin	nap	neck
nick	not	crack	nut	on	in
octagon	pass	pack	pad	pat	pal
pan	past	peg	pet	pep	pest
insect	piglatin	pink	pick	pill	pin
pit	plan	plant	plastic	pocket	pot
print	prick	pup	puppet	ran	rack
rust	rug	rut	ram	rat	rest
red	rent	rev	rip	rot	rock
rub	sad	sap	sack	sag	sand
scab	set	sell	self	help	send
seven	six	ten	sick	silk	sink
sis	skim	skin	skip	slick	slid
smell	snap	soft	sock	solid	speck
spill	spit	staff	stamp	stand	stack
stiff	stun	stuff	subject	suck	swim
swift	tack	tan	tap	tell	tent
test	tin	ticket	tilt	bend	tom
top	track	tramp	trap	trip	truck
trust	trunk	twin	twist	up	unlock
van	vomit	web	west	well	wind
wink	yes	lid	limp		

Sound out these words and join them to the part of the body named. Use the picture of the boy or girl, or both.

leg

hand

hip

back

lips

Here is a poem. Read it and look at the picture of what it means.

fog on a red hut

on a hill

cat is hidden

wind is still

Here is another poem to read. Try to act it out.

hot dog ... mmmm

hot pop ... ick

hot ham ... mmmm

hot hands ... sick

hot buns ... mmmm

hot legs ... run

hot cob ... mmmm

hot lamp ... sun

Here are some action words to read and then act out.

run   jump

dig   kick

spin   skip

rip   nod

pass   yell

at bat

CONGRATULATIONS!

You and your child have now completed level one.

Your child has learned all of the letters of the alphabet, lower case, one sound per letter.

His or her reading vocabulary is well over 600 words. He or she has learned how to read from left to right, top to bottom of a page and how to sound out words.

Your child is well on the way to becoming a competent reader.

What can you do now?

1. You can review this whole book with him or her a few pages a day. If you started the program when the child was under three, redoing level one may be a very useful review.

2. If you would like to continue and your child is keen, you can move to Level Two of the program. There your child will learn the upper case of the letters again with a logical explanation (buh got a new bump as it got older — B). Your child will learn the formal names of the letters that they yell out when they're all at a party. You will show the odd sounds some letters make when they join with 'crazy h' (sh, ch, ph, gh, th, wh), and you'll show how some of the little letters yell a new sound when they're wanting attention (ay, e, i , o, you). All of these concepts are taught in level two with stories, examples, poems and games. At the end of level two your child will have a reading vocabulary of several thousand words. At the end of level two the child is also able to learn to print the letters.

3. I recommend you continue to read stories to the child before naps and at bedtime, and that this be active reading in which you show pictures and discuss them, predict plots, and criticize good and bad points of stories, movies, TV shows. You are raising an intelligent, critical, informed reader and thinker. It is such a marvellous adventure that I kind of envy you as you proceed with it. Have fun.

ADAPTATION OF THE LETTER POEM
FOR THOSE WITH HEARING CHALLENGES

The letter poem can also be used to link the American Sign Language sign for each letter with the shape of the letter and the sound it makes.

huh is for house	The two fingers sticking out have one shorter than the other, as a house with a chimney viewed from the side.
muh is for mittens	Three bumps of three knuckles — bump-a-bump.
puh — pretty flower	Two fingers sticking into the ground to test the soil. Thumb in middle touches a pretty flower.
suh — snake is bitten	Fist is clenched to protect self from snake.
wuh is for waves	Three fingers shape waves, wuh, and boat must go up and down.
tuh for train	Tracks thumb is stuck tight between two knuckles like train is riding between tracks.
ruh — round the corner	Forefinger is trying to round the corner and middle finger is trying to prevent it.
ah — apple stacks	Thumb is poking into a stack of apples.
buh — bump on bottom	Hand has thumb making bump on bottom.
cuh is for curl	Hand forms curl shape.
duh is for doorknob	Hand shapes doorknob and door.
guh — long-haired girl	Hand signal is a gesture to show. "Don't cut off too much hair cause I want it this long."
nuh — nail got bent	Two fingers are sides of bent nail.
ih — it jumped up	Baby finger jumped up.
eh — egg fell open right into a cup	Hand acts out crack in egg.
oh (aw) is for octopus	Fingers shape O and knuckles suggest many legs of octopus.
uh — under umbrella	Forefinger is person standing and middle finger is umbrella he is under.

165

fuh has a funny top. *He's a strange fella.*	Hand signal is everything is "fine" — He feels happy.
juh — just a jet's trail	Baby finger traces jet trail in air.
kuh — kite on string	Forefinger is man standing, middle finger is kite with string.
luh is for ladder. *You climb it in spring.*	Forefinger is ladder and thumb is base extended for balance, or is the ground.
vuh is for very good	Fingers shape victory sign.
yuh — yarn with tail *you see*	Thumb and baby finger are far apart to hold large length of yarn and not get it knotted up.
zuh is for zigzag you draw when you feel happy	Happy zigzag drawn in air.
ex is for crossing *the street where* *you've been*	First finger bent is small person waiting to cross the street and putting arm out to show he is crossing (viewed from side).
kwuh (q) is a *lady with long dress,* *a queen.*	Thumb and first finger point to ground to indicate the royal lady's long gown with train.

Note to Parent   *For children with learning delays*

The program may well suit your needs in its progression, but you may need to review each page more before proceeding. Children with coordination problems may still be able to sound out words if you as a parent point to the letters and pictures.

For children in bilingual programs

Most sounds in French, Spanish, and German are similar to those of the English alphabet. There are a few exceptions, often vowels, but more is the same than that that is different. If the child's community or first language is English, I recommend introducing hom or her to reading this as a parallel to any other language being taught. There may be small, temporary areas of confusion, but children are very adept at learning languages well. To delay instruction of one's native language gives a child an unnecessary obstacle.

Lesson 17

Do you remember our poem?

> huh is for house
> muh is for mittens
> puh pretty flower
> suh snake is bitten
>
> wuh is for waves
> tuh for traintracks
> ruh — round the corner
> ah — apple stacks
>
> buh — bump on bottom
> cuh is for curl
> duh is for doorknob
> guh — long-haired girl
>
> nuh — nail got bent
> ih — it jumped up
> eh — egg fell open right into a cup
>
> oh (aw) is for octopus
> uh — under umbrella
> fuh has a funny top. He's a strange fella.
>
> juh — just a jet's trail
> kuh — kite on string
> luh is for ladder. You climb it in spring.
>
> vuh is for very good
> yuh — yarn with tail you see
> zuh is for zigzag you draw when you feel happy.
>
> ex is for crossing the street where you've been
> kwuh (q) is a lady with long dress, a queen.

167

Capital Letters

Now you know all the little letters. We are going to look at what happens when they grow into big letters. Just as children grow up to be adults who are taller, the little letters grow up too.

Some look just like the little ones, only bigger.

c   becomes   C

Draw a line from the letter on the left to the way it looks when it grows up on the right.

v   C

w   Z

x   X

z   V

c   W

Look at the letter on the left and circle the one along the same line that is the same as the one on the left.

V | W V X

X | T H X

W | W V M

Z | S Z U

P | B P B

Look at the picture on the left and then join it to the letter on the right that starts its name.

Look at the letter on the left and circle the one along the same line that looks the same.

C	O	C	D
O	O	D	C
K	T	V	K
P	B	P	B
S	C	D	S

Read the word on the left and join it to the picture it is talking about. You will notice that the words now start with a big letter.

Zip

Wig

Vest

Can

Lesson 18

Here are the little letters that look the same only bigger when they grow up. We are going to put together a poem to remember them.

C
P
O
X
W

Capital Letters Poem

Cuh is still a curl, you see;
Kuh is still a kite.
Pretty flower is just the same,
Snakes stay snakes at night.

Oh is oh even when big,
Very good's not changed.
X-rays look the same when big
Zigzag's not rearranged.

And Wuh is not wasting
the energy's he's saving.
wuh stays the same and
he just keeps on waving.

K
S
V
Z

Lesson 19

When some of the little letters grew up though, they changed a bit.

Little ih was still jumping up, and now he's got a hat, and to balance, he stuck his feet out on each side.

Little juh was still a jet's trail, but now the dot on top has stretched out and entered a cloud. He looks like he has a hat too.

Circle the big ihs in this row.

I I i I

Circle the big juhs in this row.

J j j J

174

On this page circle all of the big letters, the way they look when they grow up. They are called capital letters by some people, but you don't have to call them that if you don't want to.

c k p W

w z x O

i j I

K S o

175

Now see if you can match the families. Look at the letter on the left and join it with a line to the way it looks when it has grown.

j   K

k   S

s   O

i   I

o   J

Read the word on the left and join it to the picture of what it means on the right. You will notice that now the words start with a big letter.

Jug

Inn

Van

Sometimes the little letters had to have hooks sticking out of them to help them balance.

Well, when they grew up, they didn't need those helpers any more. They straightened up.

traintracks lost a section.

 became

under now stood alone, without a curl at the bottom.

 became

yarn, with the long tail sticking out, was able to stand up so that its tail was now straight down.

 became

fuh with funny top lost his funny top, and it straightened out nicely, but all on one side.

 became

Our Capital Letters Poem

Now we can add to the poem about how the letters grew up.

Cuh is still a curl you see;
Kuh is still a kite.
Pretty flower is just the same,
Snakes stay snakes at night.

C K P S

Oh is oh even when big,
Very good's not changed.
X-rays look the same when big,
Zigzag's not rearranged.

O V X Z

And Wuh is not wasting
the energy's he's saving.
wuh stays the same and
he just keeps on waving.

W

Juh jumped up and got a hat;
Ih got a hat, too.
Traintracks didn't need their extra section
— well wouldn't you?

J I T

Under stands well now alone.
Yuh yarn's so big it won't lie down.
Fuh's funny top got very straight
It's sort of like a crown.

U Y F

In this row circle the big tuhs.

T t T f T

In this row circle the big uhs.

U V U v u

In this row circle the big yuhs.

y Y y Y v

Now circle the big fuhs in this row.

F f t f F

Join the big capital letter on the left with the way it used to look when it was little, on the right.

U

J

T

Y

F

f

y

u

t

j

Join the letter on the left with the one on the right that is its big version.

c

J

p

T

s

P

t

C

j

S

Read the words on the left and join each one to the picture of it they mean. Notice how the words now start with a big letter.

Yell

Fan

Up

Some Letters Get Tall

When the little letters got big, they were much taller. Little ih, for instance, now had trouble getting through doorways with his hat on.

i

So sometimes, ih, when it is a big letter, takes off its hat.

I

We already know a letter that looks like that, don't we? It's little luh, ladder. But you won't get them mixed up. You'll know which one is which from the words they are in.

legs

When little juh left the jet's trail and flew into a cloud, that was fun.

J

But sometimes it was sunny out and juh hit no cloud. It just kept going up.

J

But they are still the same letter. That's for sure. They just sometimes take their hats off.

I J

Lesson 20

Some of the little letters grew big in other ways. Just like a person might get a bit heavier, some of the letters put on things.

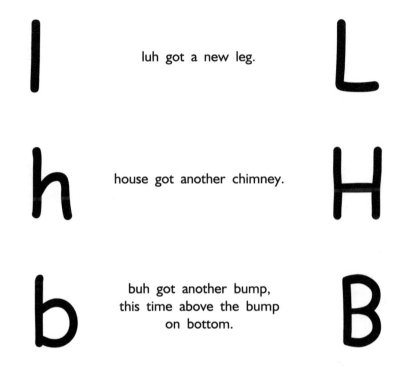

l   luh got a new leg.   L

h   house got another chimney.   H

b   buh got another bump,
this time above the bump
on bottom.   B

Circle all the letters below that are big letters that we call capital letters.

b   B   L   H

h   B   b   L

185

Join the big letter on the left with the way it used to look when little, the one on the right.

B

I

L

y

H

b

Y

h

Read the word on the left and join it to the picture of what it means. You can see that sometimes words now start with big letters.

Hat

Lamp

Bug

Capital Letters Poem

Now we can add even more to our poem about how the letters grew up.

Cuh is still a curl, you see;
Kuh is still a kite.
Pretty flower is just the same,
Snakes stay snakes at night.

C K P S

Oh is oh even when big,
Very good's not changed.
X-rays look the same when big,
Zigzag's not rearranged.

O V X Z

W

And Wuh is not wasting
the energy's he's saving.
wuh stays the same and
he just keeps on waving.

Juh jumped up and got a hat;
Ih got a hat, too.
Traintracks didn't need their extra section
— well wouldn't you?

J I T

Under stands well now alone.
Yuh yarn's so big it won't lie down.
Fuh's funny top got very straight
It's sort of like a crown.

U Y F

Buh bump on bottom got bumpy on top,
Ladder got a new leg.
Huh house got chimney too,
It's made of a straight peg.

B L H

Some of the little letters that used to be curved straightened out as they grew big.

e

egg fell open in two places now.

E

n

nail got bent and had to be pushed up again.

N

Circle the big letters below.

E   F   e   B

N   n   O   s

189

Some of the little round letters got very pointy.

a

The half an apple got bitten, and now shows a big toothmark.

A

m

Mittens got frozen stiff, and the fingers of the mittens got pointed.

M

Circle the big capital letters below.

A V M o

N S p t

Capital Letters Poem

Now our poem is getting much longer

Cuh is still a curl you see;
Kuh is still a kite.
Pretty flower is just the same,
Snakes stay snakes at night.

Oh is oh even when big,
Very good's not changed.
X-rays look the same when big,
Zigzag's not rearranged.

And Wuh is not wasting
the energy's he's saving.
wuh stays the same and
he just keeps on waving.

Juh jumped up and got a hat;
Ih got a hat, too.
Traintracks didn't need their extra section
— well wouldn't you?

Under stands well now alone.
Yuh yarn's so big it won't lie down.
Fuh's funny top got very straight
It's sort of like a crown.

Buh bump on bottom got bumpy on top,
Ladder got a new leg.
Huh house got chimney too,
It's made of a straight peg.

Egg fell open in two parts now;
Nuh nail got bent and pushed back.
Mittens froze stiff with fingers up;
Ah apple got bitten in its stack.

CKPS
OVXZ
W
JIT
UYF
BLH
ENMA

191

Join the small letter on the left with the big one on the right that it matches. Watch for when ih and juh don't wear their hats.

c

v

i

j

t

f

F

T

J

V

C

I

Join the little letter on the left with its big capital shape, when it grew up, on the right.

u   S

s   W

w   Y

y   U

x   X

Join the small letter on the left with the way it looks on the right when it grew up.

b   H

h   B

l   L

a   A

Read the words on the left and match them to the picture of their meaning on the right. Notice how you are now reading words that start sometimes with big letters.

Man

Egg

Bed

Lesson 21

Little duh for doorknob also grew up, but in a strange way. It got smashed through the door,

and the hole got much bigger,

d

so big duh is like a hole on the side of a door.

D

Circle the big duhs below.

D

O

C

B

D

quh queen had a long dress already when she was little. Now that she got big though, she got very, very round and her dress now looks quite a bit shorter, doesn't it?

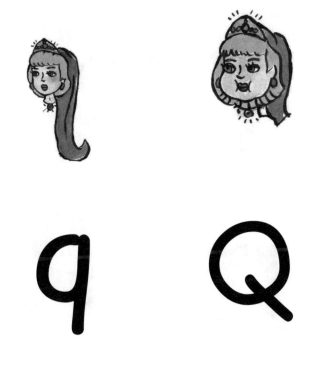

Circle the big quhs.

Do you remember little ruh who ran round the corner? When he grew big he had run all around that corner and headed back, nearly home, and then he decided to go out wandering some more. Here is how his path looks when he is big.

r became R

Circle the big ruhs below.

r R B D

R b d r

Girl with long hair did an amazing trick as she got bigger. She stood on her head,

g

so now, big guh looks like this.

G

Circle the big guhs below.

g G p G q

Circle the big letters in the line below watching for guh, quh and ruh's tricks.

Q R r q G

Read the words on the left and join them to the word on the right showing what they mean.

Run

Dog

Gum

Capital Letters Poem

Here is our capital letters poem now. We can see how every letter grew up. As you hear the poem point to the letter on the side that we are talking about.

Cuh is still a curl, you see;
Kuh is still a kite.
Pretty flower is just the same,
Snakes stay snakes at night.

C K P S

Oh is oh even when big,
Very good's not changed.
X-rays look the same when big,
Zigzag's not rearranged.

O V X Z

And Wuh is not wasting
the energy's he's saving.
wuh stays the same and
he just keeps on waving.

W

Juh jumped up and got a hat;
Ih got a hat, too.
Traintracks didn't need their extra section
— well wouldn't you?

J I T

Under stands well now alone.
Yuh yarn's so big it won't lie down.
Fuh's funny top got very straight
It's sort of like a crown.

U Y F

Buh bump on bottom got bumpy on top,
Ladder got a new leg.
Huh house got chimney too,
It's made of a straight peg.

B L H

Egg fell open in two parts now;
Nuh nail got bent and pushed back.
Mittens froze stiff with fingers up;
Ah apple got bitten in its stack.

E N M A

The duh doorknob hole has gone right through.
Girl with long hair turned upside down.
Quh queen got fat and her dress got short
Ruh round the corner walked back to the ground.

D G Q R

Note to Parent:

1. The child now has been taught all the upper case letters as well as the lower case.

2. These letters are still pronounced ah, buh, cuh, and not by their formal names ay, bee, see.

3. Many commercial sets of letters are actually capital letters only. You were only able to use those letters which looked the same in lower case — c k p s o v x z w. Sometimes you could use k, depending on how high the second arm went. Now, however, you can use all the letters in the set. They can be found in toy stores in magnet form, in plastic, in fabric, in wood. They can be found in edible form in some alphabet soups and cereals, as well as individually in large chocolate units. You will find lots of them in drugstores and other general stores as stamps for doorknob labels. I encourage you to purchase a few of these and let the child play with them (making sure, of course, to avoid choking hazard if the letter is small). You could also make your own capital letters out of Mactac, sponge, sandpaper, cardboard, Plasticene, pipe cleaners, or wet noodles.

   The point is that kids love to actually feel the letters and manipulate them. In this way you help them remember the shape of the letter, not just visually but also with tactile clues. Remember that the letter has to be still in very tall format, in large font, so that the child can identify its fine details.

4. From now on you can label the child's parcels and drawings and some of his or her toys with the child's name spelled using a capital for first letter. (It is quite possible his name contains some exceptions to our rules, but he is probably so impatient to see his name that you can gloss over the exceptions and he can learn his own name as something special.)

5. On outings, continue to point out letters and to sound out words wherever they do not use exceptions to the basic rules already known (no silent letters or long vowels yet). You can trace letters in snow, in sand at the park, in flour on the kitchen table, in icing, in the deep pile of carpet samples. Remember that the small child cannot himself print the letter dependably, so don't expect him to do it right if he tries. I like to praise kids to the skies for any effort, even if the child actually has to read the letter to you for you to know what it says. The skill of printing is a separate skill.

6. Label things around the house as before, but now sometimes using a capital letter at the start: e.g., Bed, Rug, Lamp, Melissa's Bed.

7. There is much he can read now, and much he can't. Again, only show him material at which he can succeed. This makes him feel competent.

The Letter Party

Little eh decided to have a party.

He invited many letters and his house was soon full of them. They each came over to say hello to him, and he handed them chocolate eggs and candy. But such a big crowd gathered around him that some of them couldn't get through to him at all.

Poor little eh was surrounded by letters.

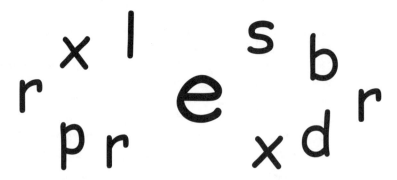

When ah couldn't get through to him because another letter was in the way,

he finally shouted, "GET OUT OF THE WAY!"
The sound echoed, and everybody heard ah say, "OUT OF THE WAY AY AY AY."

So now, whenever a letter comes between ah and eh, the ah will often yell "GET OUT OF THE WAY, AY," and eventually just "ay."

This makes eh so surprised he just sits there and stays quiet.

ate

This word says, "get out of the way-ay" — tuh — and eh is quiet.
So it says, ay tuh — ate.

In the words below you will see that ah also yells, "Get out of the way, ay." Sound out the words and then join them to the pictures of their meanings. Remember that when eh hears ah yelling, he stays quiet.

gate

ape

lake

name

Jim

Read these words below and join them to their meanings on the right. Remember how ah yells "ay," and little eh is so surprised, he's quiet.

cane

skate

plate

crane

grapes

In these words draw a circle around the letter that comes between ah and eh. It's the one that's in the way. The first one is done for you.

g(av)e

take

bake

made

brave

Draw a circle around the letter that comes between ah and eh. Remember, it's the one that's in the way.

ape

cane

gate

name

skate

When there is no letter in the way, then ah still says ah.

Read these words below and join them to the pictures of their meaning.

cane

can

cap

cape

Read the words below and match them to their meanings. Remember to see if there is a letter in the way for ah to yell at.

tap

tape

hat

hate

At the letter party the letter yuh was hanging around too.
It liked to hook up its yarn near the other letters
and some of them were angry.

ay

When yuh got near ah, sometimes ah would yell his old, "GET OUT OF THE WAY, AY."

Here are some words where ah is so mad at yuh beside him that he yells, "AY,"
and yuh is so shocked, he gets quiet.

See if you can read them out loud.

pay   puh — get out of the way AY
             puh ay   pay

pay

hay

Monday

say

May

211

Read the words below. You will see that ah is again yelling "AY," like in "GET OUT OF THE WAY."

Join the words to the pictures of what they mean.

crayon

hay

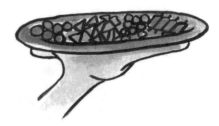

tray

spray

Here is a new game. On one side we see words with a picture to show what they mean. On the other side are just words.

Sound out all the words on the left side and notice what they mean.

Now sound out the words on the right side, and find the ones that mean the same as the ones on the left. Join the words that mean just about the same thing.

cap

bug

pig

mug

ant

hog

cup

hat

213

Lesson 22

Do you remember the letter party? Little e was still often surrounded by letters and he felt very small. Nobody could see him well. He would try to get others to see over heads and find him by yelling, "It's ME ME ME," and the room would echo "EEEE."

Sometimes, when eh is all alone, he remembers how small he felt, and he yells out so others will still notice him. He yells, "It's MEEEE," and you can just hear "EEEE."

e

Here are some words where eh is yelling "EEEE." See if you can read them.

we   he   be   me

When yuh was at the party he was up to his old tricks, trying to hook his yarn into the other letters, especially the little ones. Little eh got mad at him for hooking on, and called out to others to still notice he was there. "It's MEEEE."

So sometimes, when eh and yuh are beside each other,

ey

eh is yelling EEEE and yuh is quiet.

key

It is hard to be so small. When little eh finally meets another little eh, he is so happy he nearly dances with excitement. Both little ehs yell out "HAPPY TO MEEEET YOU. HAPPY TO SEEEEE YOU," and the room echoes with the noise they are making, "EEEE."

So sometimes when you see two little ehs together, they are yelling "EEEE."
Here is a word where that happens.
tuh   ruh   happy to meeeet you — tuh ruh eeee — tree

ee

tree

Read the words on the left and join them to the pictures of what they mean. You will notice that little ehs are happily calling out, "HAPPY TO MEET YOU EEEE."

tree

deer

seed

bee

freeway

Read these words and join them to the picture of what they mean.

feet

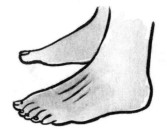

heel

beet

weed

key

Here is a new game that's tricky but fun. On the right you can see four pictures.

On the left are four sentences. You read the words in each line and then join the whole set of the words on the line to the picture of what they mean.

See a jeep

It is a deer

See a pup

A tree is here

217

At the letter party there was a lot of noise.

ah was saying, "GET OUT OF THE WAY, AY."

eh was saying, "IT'S ME, IT'S ME, EEEE."

a
e

Now little ih was sad because he was so small that no one noticed him. So he decided that whenever he was alone, he'd stretch into a big letter so he could be seen better.

i   I

And he decided he'd be friendlier and yell out, "HI, HI," and soon the room echoed, "I."

I

Little ih also decided that if a letter got between him and eh, he'd just yell out so eh could still see him and give him chocolate eggs.

Well, when ih was yelling like that, "Hi, Hi," eh was so shocked he grew quiet.

In these words, little ih is yelling "Hi, I, I," and eh is so surprised he's quiet.

b
i k e
d

buh   hi — I I kuh and eh is quiet
buh eye kuh   bike

bike

Here is another word that has ih yelling, "Hi I I." Read it and look at the picture of what it means.

dime

Read these words and join them to the pictures of what they mean. Notice that sometimes little ih is yelling, "Hi, I."

kite

slide

fire

bike

Read these words and watch for little ih yelling out, "Hi." Join the words to the pictures of what they mean.

pipe

wine

five

beside

In this game, there are two words in each block, but there's only one picture. Look at the picture and then read each word. Figure out which word names the picture and then draw a circle around that word.

fin
fine

spin
spine

pin
pine

bit
bite

rid
ride

win
wine

tim
time

kit
kite

Lesson 23

Now, at the letter party, we had little eh handing out goodies and ah yelling "Get out of the way, ay." Eh sometimes yelled 'It's me, EEEE."

Ih was yelling "Hi, I,"
and little oh (aw) started to feel ignored.

o

He decided he'd be friendlier too, and he started to yell, "HELLO-O-O-O," and soon the room echoed with his "Oh-Oh-Oh' sounds.

So when little oh (aw) is at the end of a word, he sometimes says, "Oh."

Read these words.

no   go   so

When eh was giving out the candies and a letter got in the way,
little oh (aw) said his, "HELLO-O-O" very loud,
and eh was again so surprised he was quiet.

Here is a word where that happens.

ruh oh puh — roh puh — rope

Read this word.

rope

Read the word on the left and watch for when oh (aw) yells out, "Hello-oh-oh."
Join the word to the picture of what it means.

bone

Join these words to the picture of what they mean.

rope

bone

stove

home

Sometimes little oh (aw) decided that if he was surrounded by letters, he'd just yell out, "Hello-o-o-o," to make sure he was noticed.

Read these words and join them to the picture of what they mean.

cold

roll

gold

fork

In this game you see two words in each set, but only one of them goes with the picture there. Read the words, both of them, and then circle the one that names what's in the picture.

pop

pope

cod

code

glob

globe

When you are reading now, you have to watch out for tricks some of the letters play. In these words watch out for oh (aw) sometimes saying, "hello-o-o-o." Read these words and join them to the picture of what they mean.

hotel

snow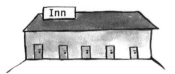

hippo

open

bowl

Now, at the letter party, we sure had a lot of noise!

ah was yelling, "GET OUT OF THE WAY, AY."

eh sometimes called, "IT'S ME, EEEE."

ih was saying, "Hi, I, I"

o (aw) was calling, "HELLO-O-O-O."

Well, there was one other little letter that was now feeling pretty much alone. Little uh wanted to yell out, too. People kept forgetting he was there, so he decided to call out, "I SEE YOU…HOW ARE YOU?" and the word echoed. "You-You-You."

So sometimes little uh says, "you."

When a letter comes between uh and eh,
while handing out candies for instance,
little uh yells, "HOW ARE YOU?" so loudly
that eh is quiet.

muh yoo luh   mule

mule

The little letters were sure getting smart now, and they didn't fall over much at all.

Little uh, for example, when he was under the umbrellas, didn't need any extra stick to lean against.

So sometimes, uh looks like this U, and other times like this u.

It's still uh.

Read these words and watch for uh's trick. Join them to the picture they describe.

cute

June

Read these words and join them to the pictures of what they mean. Remember how uh yells "How are you...you,"?

flute

tub

tube

mule

In this game, there are two words, but there's only one picture again. Read both words and circle the one that names what's in the picture.

tub
tube

cub
cube

cut
cute

At the very noisy letter party we now had five letters yelling. Those little letters were yelling a new sound.

In fact, we now have five letters that can each say TWO different things.

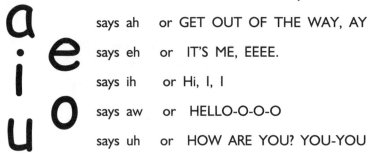

a says ah or GET OUT OF THE WAY, AY

e says eh or IT'S ME, EEEE.

i says ih or Hi, I, I

o says aw or HELLO-O-O-O

u says uh or HOW ARE YOU? YOU-YOU

The room was too noisy. Little eh's friends had a solution. They would give all those little letters special attention by lining them up, sitting them down, and giving them something yummy so they'd stop yelling.

ah is yelling, "Get out of the way."
eh is yelling 'It's me. It's me."
ih is screaming "Hi. Hi."
and aw is calling "Hello," with glee.

uh is shouting, "How are you?"
And what is anyone else to do?
Now everyone saying A E I O U
We'll call you all VOWELS — that's what we'll do.

We'll sit you all down
And if you just don't scream
We'll bring you five special
big bowls of ice cream.

Note to Parent: The child now has been taught the long sounds of the vowels as well as the short sounds from earlier. This will have tremendously increased his/her range of words. However, do not assume that the child will automatically get the idea. Practice is needed. It is not necessary to remind the child of the rules about a letter getting in the way too often. It is enough if the child simply tries out one sound the letter can make, and if that doesn't work, tries out another.

Here are some words you can print around the house. Remember to print them in a font large enough that the child's eye can see the fine details easily. Remember to use the font with a g t to make sure you don't confuse the child yet with extra curls. You can, however, sometimes use upper case letters now if you wish, but remember that in school the child will mostly use lower case.

Here is a partial list of words the child can now, with help, read. Do not expect the child to read them all, but you might want to put a few on papers or write them on a blackboard once in a while.

Activity suggestions:

1. You can print the words on sheets around the house.

2. You could make a little book of one word per page and have the child illustrate the word after he or she reads it.

3. You could write a book with one word per page, maybe thirty words in all, and then draw what they mean, incorporating the child's suggestions and then let the child colour the picture.

tub	tube	cub	cube	cut	cute
rule	Yule	Yukon	duke	tune	uke
mule	flute	me	I	so	he
we	hi	student	pupil	June	spoke
Joe	Pete	open	gold	stone	note
hippo	bone	broken	pole	sore	nose
hole	old	rope	window	hello	horse
corn	sofa	fork	snow	hotel	bowl
Otto	Cora	Nora	Norma	Lorette	Doris
yellow	motel	slow	zone	before	for
bold	hold	program	cone	pope	hope
rode	behind	inside	until	sold	post
told	Toronto	six o'clock	ten o'clock	seven	Simon
Ida	smile	bike	slide	nineteen	hike

231

Here are some more words you can print around the house or in books to illustrate or colour. Don't try to do them all, and remember the child can't print these words herself yet. Just help her read them and, of course, praise her efforts and give rewards.

like	lemonade	parade	file	stiff	time
pine	mine	wild	mild	mind	drive
kind	dime	side	wine	fine	bite
spoke	spine	spin	kit	kite	five
pipe	wife	fire	Friday	Lee	make
heel	fed	sweep	feed	feet	get
pet	sleep	see	sees	bee	sweet
jeep	creek	eel	asleep	speed	street
seed	geese	sixteen	seventeen	eleven	Steven
Eva	green	Vera	defend	reflect	between
develop	begin	demand	depend	Abe	cake
take	fake	lake	make	sake	rake
fade	made	wade	ale	male	pale
sale	tale	fame	game	name	same
tame	ape	cape	tape	bare	care
dare	mare	rare	stare	spare	base
case	ate	Kate	gate	late	mate
rate	brave	crave	bay	day	gay
hay	lay	may	pay	say	way
be	fee	pee	reed	deed	feed
need	weed	beef	beer	feel	been
teen	beep	keep	deep	weep	deer
beet	meet	bride	pride	hide	ride
side	tide	wide	life	hike	like
mike	pike	yikes	file	mile	Nile
pile	tile	dime	lime	mime	time
crime	dine	fine	line	mine	nine
pine	mind	bind	kind	find	hind
rind	ripe	fire	hire	tire	lite

Here are a few more words and expressions you can put up around the house. Again, don't try to do them all.

go	no	globe	robe	Coke	poke
code	rode	hole	mole	pole	dome
home	bone	lone	tone	hope	mope
rope	bore	more	sore	tore	dose
note	cube	tube	sub	tub	Erica
Bob	David	Ed	Gus	Jen	Krista
Karen	Len	Matt	Norm	Pat	Sam
Tom	Will				

He can see a rope.

Can Don go in?

Ten pups jump on a bed.

Six ducks swim in a lake.

Get up at six.

We can get a cone.

I ride fast on a bike.

Have fun with it and remember to stop when the child is tired of the game each day. This is supposed to be fun.

Meanwhile, move ahead with the program.

Lesson 24

At the letter party, one of the letters got jealous.

y

yuh figured that if so many letters had two sounds they could make, why couldn't he?

He decided to show off and do a trick. He threw one arm up into the air and twisted it into a dot and said what ih says, "Hi, I, I."

I

So sometimes, especially when yuh is at the end of a word, instead of yuh he will say, "Hi, I, I."

Here is a word where he does that:

muh   eye   my

my

Here is another: buh eye   by

by

Read the words and join them to the picture of what they mean.

fly

cry

Read the words on the left. Each one is an action. Read each action and join the word that matches. Find something that can:

fly

cry

dry

fry

Read these words below and join them to the picture of what they mean.

my dog

my cat

myself

fire hydrant

At the letter party, yuh could now twist around and yell, "Hi, I, I," sometimes.

But was that enough for him? No!

He tried another trick. He twisted both arms and stretched around till he made himself an eh. And then he decided he could yell out what eh yells, "It's ME-EEEE."

Here is a word where yuh calls out "EEEE"

huh ah puh puh eeee happpeeee   happy

happy

Read these words and join them to what they mean.

baby

lady

Read the words on the left and join them to the pictures of what they mean. Watch out for the tricks the letters do now. Remember how yuh can call out, "EEEE."

candy

pony

jelly

lady

baby

Now we know that the letter yuh can do lots of tricks.

Sometimes it says, yuh like in 'yes'.

Sometimes it says "Hi, I, I" like in 'cry'.

Sometimes it says, "EEEE" like in 'baby'.

Y
e I

So when you see yuh, you have to try out a few sounds and see which sound it's making today. Read these words below and join them to what they mean.

penny

bunny

piggy

poppy

Read these words below and join them to what they mean.

funny

foggy

windy

puppy

Here are some words that the child can sound out now with help.
Draw what the word means.

puppy

kitty

candy

Lesson 25

At the letter party the letters were all having a great time now. They were eating and yelling and somebody got out balloons. In fact, one little oh (aw) crept up on another and bumped him with one, and yelled, "Boo!"

So when two o(aw)s are together they sometimes say "BOO...OOO!"

oo

Here is a word where they do that.

zuh   ooo   zoo

zoo

Read these words and join them to their meaning.

zoo

moon

spoon

broom

Now read these words and join them to what they mean. Remember how oo says "boo" to each other — ooo.

boot

goose

roof

spool

pool

The party had been going on for quite a while, and many of the letters were tired. A few wanted to sit down and sleep. Some wanted to sit down and just relax. Little oh (aw) joined with another little aw (o), and they snuggled up on the sofa and started to read a book.

oo

*When o and o got tired they **took***
*Down from the shelf a favourite **book***
*At funny parts with laughs they **shook***
*With friends it's fun to read a **book.***

So sometimes when o and o are together they make the sound in "look at the book," ooo...

Read these words and figure out what oo are saying. Join the words to the pictures of what they mean.

wood

foot

book

hoof

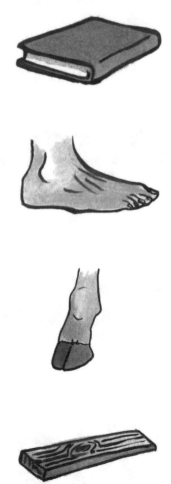

Here are some labels to cut out and put up around the house (or make new ones that are bigger).

hook   spoon

boots   broom

book   window

foot   wood

scoop   tools

Read these words and then tell the name of something that is like that. For instance, if the word is 'yellow', you could say cheese or banana. If the word is 'soft', you could say a bed or a blanket or a pillow.

Name something that is:

bumpy

lazy   cool

messy   happy

icky   muddy

angry   tiny

Here are some actions you can read and then act out.

cook	jump
swim	sleep
wake	cry
sit	stand
yell	be sad
be glad	bend
shrug	fly
dive	skate
run	hide

Note to Parent: Here are some more activities you could do now. Make sure to only use words that follow the rules we have taught to date.

1. Occasionally children enjoy having a letter or word printed right on their skin in washable ink or crayon. It washes off, and it sure is handy if they want to look at it. I would suggest you print only one word or two, but any word the child can now read is possible.

    e.g.,   't' on his tummy   'f' on a finger
            'left' on his left arm   'hand'
            'foot'   'leg'

    You can also use masking tape and print a letter or even a whole word on objects.

book	wagon	bike
skates	boots	hats

2. You can leave notes around the house, on the fridge, on a black-board, taped to a door, for the child to read.

I am happy	Open Here
bedroom	playroom
stay in bed late	get up
look here	go left

3. You can take some plastic or wood cubes, or make some out of cardboard, and then put a letter on each side. Then let your child line the blocks up to make words. You can create many words that the child can read with three blocks, for instance.

On the first put the letters	s t b r
On another put the letters	a e o u
On another put the letters	t d g m

You can ask the child to line up the blocks and read you words he can make, or you can tell the child a word and ask him to make the blocks say it. Here are some words that are useful this way

sat	sad	sag	sam	tad	tag
tan	bad	bed	rat	tag	ram
ted	bet	beg	red	tot	tom
rod	tug	but	bug	bum	rug

Names of the Letters

We saw that at the party five of the letters, ah, eh, ih, oh and uh, all had other sounds they could make. These letters were so happy with their new sounds that they decided to use them as their names.

So they became:

ay	ee	eye	oh	you
a	e	i	o	u

But that made all the other letters jealous. Why couldn't everybody get names?

Little eh had an idea. He was the one who had the party, so he said he'd join with some of the letters to help them make a name.

So eh joined with muh to make em.

e	m	em
e	n	en
e	f	ef
e	l	el
e	s	es
e	x	ex

Eh was tired from all that work. He liked helping other letters make their names, but he needed help. Another eh came along and said that the two of them together could say, "Happy to SEE you, happy to MEET you."

ee

So a few more letters joined up with EEEE that way, to make names.

b   ee   bee

d   ee   dee

p   ee   pee

t   ee   tee

v   ee   vee

z   ee   zee
(or zed)

You now know the names for many letters as well as their sounds.

Just as buh says buh, but its name is bee, you can now try to remember what the name is of these letters.

Remember the sound of the letters below, and now their name.

a	u	f
n	m	e
t	d	z
b	o	x
p	v	
e	t	

A lot of the letters now had real names of their very own. But a few didn't.

Eh was too tired to help any more, so little ah said he'd help.
He'd say "Get out of the way, ay," after some of the letters.

j a

jay
j

k a

kay
k

Then little uh said that he could help out too. He'd say, "How are You? You-You," after q (kw).

k
q u

kyoo
q

Then a funny thing happened. wuh decided, because he was tired, he'd let two uhs speak for him, each saying 'How are you? You-You." It would be a double-you.

And so wuh became named double-you.

w uu w

253

Now you know the names of even more letters. Name the ones below out loud.

Remember to tell not the sound they make, like buh, or fuh, but their new name.

j   d   w

k   u   f

a   q   b

n   e

There were now a few letters left that had no name.

huh was sitting and getting restless. This was taking too long. He started to itch. Other letters laughed and said, "Oh, itch itch itch," and huh laughed and said his name would be like that — aytch.

h

Little ruh thought this was getting silly. "What ARE you doing? What ARE you doing?" he asked. And people decided to call him "ARE."

r

Two little letters said, "What about us?"
and the others answered, "Gee, we didn't see you?

So one of them, guh, got named jee,

g c

g

and one, little cuh, got named see.

c

Yuh, who already had a sound, yuh,
and could say "ee" and "eye,"
asked what his name would be.
He was also angry they were leaving him out.
"WHY am I always the last one?" he asked.
And when he asked "WHY," they said 'We'll name you why."

y

So yuh's name became why.

And now all the letters had their own names. They could go together to do the alphabet song. See if you can read them as you sing it.

abcdefg
hijklmnop
qrstuvwxyz

Here are some messages you can read now in a secret code. You just name the letters one at a time. If they have a dot after them you can just say the name.

Try it. Do you know what these mean?

U.S.

T.V.

A.B.C.

I.O.U.

Note to Parent: Your child now knows the formal alphabet. Many parents, as you probably know, teach the young child the letter names in the alphabet song very early. That's okay.

However, in this program we showed the child one sound per letter more gradually for actually teaching reading; and we taught the sound, not the name of the letter.

At this point, though, the child has both skills. The child has two associations for each letter — its sound he learned much earlier, and its **name**. This is a small source of confusion and if the child says one for the other, he or she is not 'wrong'. You can point out that both answers are correct, but that when we read a word we use the sound not the name.

Your child also knows two shapes for many letters — both upper case and lower case. We needed to teach these because, obviously, he will need to know both. It is normal if some capital letters still sometimes confuse the child. It means he or she has both associations. But as we go on, we will continue to use mostly lower case, because that is what most books use.

Lesson 26

Crazy Huh

h is a crazy letter. You never know what he's going to do next. He's the kind of letter who hides behind a door and jumps out to scare you as you walk by. He's always into mischief.

One day huh grabbed suh and suddenly shook him,

h

and you could hear the shshshshshaking sound.
So sometimes, when suh and huh are together,
they say sh sh sh sh.

sh

Here are some words where this happens.
Read them and join each one to the picture of what it means.

ship

shell

shelf

Read these words and join them to the picture of what they mean.

dish

cash

sheep

sheet

fish

Read the words below and join them to what they mean. Notice how huh likes to take the suh and shake it.

shed

shave

dash

shaggy

Crazy huh is up to more mischief.
He likes to take the suh and shake it.

sh

But one day he also decided he could trick little cuh. He grabbed him and started to push him around the room, imitating a train, saying, "chug a chug a chug a chug."

ch   ch
ch   ch

So sometimes, when cuh and huh are together, they make a train noise, chugging.

ch

Read the words below and join them to what they mean.

lunch

chin

Join the words below to the pictures of what they mean. Remember how crazy huh likes to take the cuh and go chug a chug around a track.

cheek

chilly

chimney

children

Read the words below and join them to the pictures of what they mean.

porch

rich

chest

chat

Here is a poem you can read to your child..

Note to Parent: A few words in this poem are departures from the strict phonics rules the child has learned, but do not present sounds the child does not know. The word chocolate, for instance may be a bit hard for the child but he is encouraged to try out the sounds he knows for a letter (in this case ah/ay) until he finds one that works.

potato chips

rich milk and chops

chocolate

and chilly pop

chipmunks cheer

and children munch

rich chunk chocolate

and much lunch

Note to Parent: Here are some more words to put up around the house. Print them in a larger font, but with the same letter shape as below. Now that the child knows long sounds of vowels, new sounds of y, sounds of oo and sh and ch combinations, his reading vocabulary is getting huge.

silly	try	by	cake	duck	shape
ship	shock	dish	cash	dash	fish
wish	fresh	crash	flash	trash	brush
gush	rush	blush	crush .	shack	shed
shell	shock	shop	shot	shut	shook
shoot	book	boom	boot	cool	cook
food	foot	good	goof	hood	hoof
hoot	look	moon	noon	pool	poof
poor	roof	room	root	soon	tool
took	toot	wood	woof	zoom	broom
crooked	stool	stood	fly	fry	dry
baby	baggy	crazy	daddy	happy	lady
lately	saggy	yucky	mucky	belly	jelly
tiny	wine	tape	kitty	pity	Betty
Bobby	hobby	body	foggy	soggy	rocky
dolly	Molly	Holly	Tommy	bossy	potty
tubby	buddy	muddy	buggy	lucky	hilly
lily	tummy	bunny	funny	penny	fussy
nutty	sloppy	chest	chips	chick	chill
chin	chop	chubby	chug	ranch	branch
bench	pinch	bunch	lunch		

Have the child select one word from each column below and then have three words across and then act out the result or draw it: e.g., a black dog.

a	red	dog
my	black	hat
	candy	cane
	sloppy	fish
	fat	dolly
	yucky	lunch
	yellow	brush
	lucky	penny
	stinky	room
	broken	boot

Lesson 27

Crazy huh was loving these games.
Not only did he take the suh and shake it,

or take the cuh and make it
go chug chug chug,
but he now wanted to do more.

He grabbed wuh and tried to drag him off
to the ocean to see a whale.

But wuh is pretty wide and he was able to fight back. Wuh refused to go, and started to yell back so loudly that huh couldn't even be heard.

So when wuh and huh are together, they just say wuh.

Here are some words where that happens. Read the word and join it to the picture of what it means.

sh

ch

wh

wh

whisk

whale

Read each block on the left and then the block beside it on the right. Some of the words together will make an idea but a few words are not needed. Put a circle around the word you need to finish the idea correctly. The first one is done for you.

(when) which	at five
sit for a	while white
an egg is	which white
He is sad.	Why? Which?

Here is our poem so far about crazy huh.

He likes to take the suh and shake it
Likes to take the cuh and make it
Go a chug-a-chug-a-chug-a down the track.
Takes the wuh to see a whale
But it cannot tell its tale
Cause the wuh will yell so loud
It can't talk back.

Read the words below and join them to the picture of what they mean.

ship

whip

children

Crazy huh next decided to grab puh and roll it on the floor to flatten it. Then he pushed puh into a telephone.

ph

So when huh means puh, little puh is terrified and yells, "Not the phone, phone, phone!"

And ph together sometimes makes the found fffff, from phone.

ph   f

Here are some words where crazy huh makes puh so squished he yells "fffff."
Read these words and join them to their pictures.

phone

elephant

Read the words below and join them to the pictures of what they mean.

chipmunk

photo

fish

shake

Philip

alphabet

abcdefg
hijklmnop
qrstuvwxyz

Crazy huh wanted to do more tricks. Here is the poem so far.

He likes to take the suh and shake it
Likes to take the cuh and make it
Go a chug-a-chug-a-chug-a down the track.
Takes the wuh to see a whale
But it cannot tell its tale
Cause the wuh will yell so loud
It can't talk back.
Pushes puh into a phone

sh
ch
wh
ph

Now crazy huh had another idea. Why not grab little guh?

He sneaked up behind the girl with long hair, but she knew he was there, and she whirled around and yelled BOO to him so loud that he jumped like he'd seen a ghost.

g h

So sometimes, when guh and huh are together, guh gets to talk and huh is so surprised he's quiet.

gh

Here is a word where that happens. Read it and join it to its picture.

ghost

271

Read these words and join them to the pictures of what they mean.

ghost

chop

lunch

whale

Lesson 28

Here is the poem we have so far about Crazy Huh

> *He likes to take the suh and shake it*
> *Likes to take the cuh and make it*
> *Go a chug-a-chug-a chug-a down the track.*
> *Takes the wuh to see a whale*
> *But it cannot tell its tale*
> *Cause the wuh will yell so loud*
> *It can't talk back.*
> *Pushes puh into a phone*
> *Sees a ghost when guh's at home*

sh
ch
wh
ph
gh

But Crazy huh was not happy now. After the ghost trick he decided to grab another letter and just overpower it. He grabbed tuh.

And he threw tuh right over his back. Tuh said, "THROW me back down!" But huh just answered, "I'll throw you all right," and kept swinging him over his back. All we could hear when tuh and huh were together were the yells about throwing -th-th-th So when tuh and huh get together they sometimes say "th."

th

Here are some words where that happens. Read the words and join them to their pictures.

three

tooth

path

3

Crazy huh was finally happy. He didn't always win when he teased the other letters, but he was able to cause them to yell and there was a lot of noise. There was whistling, cheering, chugging, shaking, throwing. It was amazing.

Here is our poem about Crazy Huh.

sh

Likes to take the suh and shake it,
Likes to take the cuh and make it
Go a chug-a-chug-a-chug-a down the track,
Takes the wuh to see a whale,
But it cannot tell its tale,
'Cause the wuh will yell so loud
It can't talk back.
Pushes puh into a phone,
Sees a ghost when guh's at home,
Likes to take the tuh and throw it
On its back.
And it whistles and it cheers,
And it shouts into your ears,
As it goes a thud-a-thud-a
To its shack.

ch

wh

ph

gh

th

Read the words below and join them to the pictures of what they mean. Watch for the tricks of crazy huh.

moth

bath

274

Here are some more words you can now sound out. Read them and join them to the pictures of what they mean.

photo

path

moth

thin dog

Note to Parent: There are actually two sounds 'th' can make — as in thud and as in then. Here we are only teaching the first of these two so as not to confuse the child. The difference is very small but children are often aware of it.

Here are some expressions for the child to, with your help, read and then act out.

throw a pen

rush in

phone dad

say thanks

sit with a cat

limp

jump

smile

Read these words and join them to the pictures of what they mean.

thorn

chest

phone

chimney

Have you noticed that two of the letters we know make the same sound?

cuh curl sounds cuh.

c

and so does kuh with the boy flying a kite.

k

One day the two letters decided that they would stand together and both call out their sounds at exactly the same time. So sometimes ck says just kuh.

ck

Read these words and join them to the pictures of what they mean.

sock

block

crack

truck

Here are some more words to join to pictures of what they mean.

basket

plant

clock

blanket

snack

closet

Read the clue in the sentence while the child reads the two ways to end the sentence. The child should then circle whichever ending is better.

1. Behind your tummy is your

back
tack

2. This is a boy's name.

Jack
sack

3. A boat lands at the

clock
dock

4. Chocolate or vanilla? Take your

pick
rock

5. Which names something that swims?

duck
rock

You can now read the names of a lot of people. Sound out these

Bill

Ricky

Dave

Bobby

Sam

Ron

Brenda

Jane

Note to Parent: At this stage it is useful to let the child read the names of the people he knows. The people he lives with may have names with a few exceptions to the phonics rules, but by this stage of the program the child knows that sometimes letters have other sounds from the first few learned.

Here are some other names you could print large and have the child try. It is not necessary to do all of them. It is, however, a good idea to do a few.

Justin	Corey	Jason	Phil	Nathan
Kate	Les	Suzie	Beth	Cathy
Jenny	Fred	Melissa	Ray	Mavis
Ann	Donna	Agnes	Helen	Noreen
Doris	Ed	Ethel	Tom	Alex
Mike	Mary	Ben	Rudolph	Len
Dick	Jill	Emma	Toby	Mandy
Janet	Gus	Morris	Roland	Peggy
Andy	Meg	Jane	Elden	Devin

Match the name of the object to its usual colour.

sky	red
grass	green
fire	blue
black	pupil
yellow	sun

The Alphabet

You now know all of the letters and all of their names. You can do lots of games and puzzles now using these letters.

You can sing them.

abcdefg
hijklmnop
qrstuvwxyz

You can list foods that start with each letter, animals that start with each letter, etc. For example, apple, banana, carrot, donut,

egg, ant, bat, cat, duck, elephant.

You can join them in dot-to-dot puzzles like this.

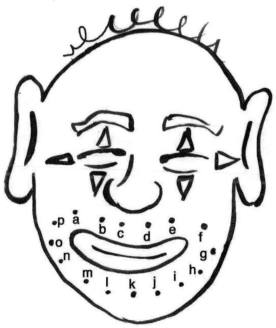

Read the hints below aloud and allow the child to then guess the word that fits the description. (Parent, print the answer or just let the child say it. He or she cannot yet print or spell the answer.)

What you eat soup with.

sp_____

Small animal that barks.

d_____

Colour of grass.

g_____

What an airplane can do.

fl_____

Lesson 29

The little letters were getting so noisy at the party that someone said there should be a few rules or nobody would be able to hear anyone else talk.

Some of the noisiest letters were the vowels.

a e i o u

Somebody had a pretty good idea. If two vowels are together they aren't both allowed to yell at the same time. Whoever got there first can talk and say its long sound and the other one has to be quiet.

Remember the vowels
Who were eating ice cream?
They're such loud little letters —
You know what I mean.
If two get together
There can be quite a fight,
And it's not at all easy
To tell who is right.
So here is the way
They decided to try it.
The first one yells out,
And the second is quiet.

ie ae
oe ou
ai ui

In each pair below circle the first letter. It is the one that gets to talk. The other one is quiet.

ai ui oa

285

Here are two of the fighting vowels:

ea

They agreed that the first one could talk and the next would be quiet. So eh yells, "It's me, it's me," and ah says nothing.

Read the words below and join them to the pictures of what they mean.

seal

eat

hello

ear

speak

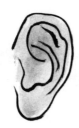

Read the words below and join them to the pictures of what they mean.

leaf

meat

tea

tears

peanuts

Read the words below and join them to the pictures of what they mean. Remember that when two vowels are together, the first one talks and the next one is quiet.

a real cat

seat

beach

eat

peacock

Here are two more vowels that we have to keep from fighting.

ai

The first one yells, "Get out of the way, ay ay," and the other is quiet.

Read these words and join them to what they mean.

train

chain

sail

rain

289

Read the words below and join them to the pictures of what they mean. Remember that the first vowel talks, and the next one is quiet.

nail

tail

mail

pail

maid

Read the words below and join them to the pictures of what they mean.

stairs

hair

chair

pair

Lesson 30

When oh gets with another vowel he has to follow the rule too. Oh gets to yell, "Hello-O-O-O," and the other vowel is quiet.

oa

Circle the vowel in each set that is allowed to talk.

oa   ou   oe

Read the words below and join them to the picture they match.

toe

boat

four

Read these words below and join them to the picture they match.

goat

hoe

road

raincoat

Read the words below and join them to the picture they match.

toad

toast

four

railroad

Here we see little ih. When it is first, next to another vowel, it gets to yell, "Hi, I, I," while the other letter is quiet.

ie

Read the words below and join them to the picture they match.

pie

tie

seal

coat

Here is another pair of vowels. In this set the first one is eh, so it gets to yell, "It's me, EEEE," while the next one is quiet.

ei

Read these words and join them to the picture they match.

Sheila

Neil

weird

When little uh got next to another vowel he got to yell, "How are you? You-You," while the other vowel was quiet.

ui   ue

Read the words below and match them to the pictures.

glue

swimsuit

fruit

snowsuit

Match the name of the object to its usual colour.

sky   yellow

sun   black

grass   blue

bugs   green

Read these signs and stick them up around the house.

FOR SALE

Staff Only

Phone

Wet Paint

Wait Here

Get Well Soon

Lesson 31

At the Dentist's

Little a was having a problem with his teeth. He had to go to the dentist and when he got there the dentist said, "Open wide. Say AW."

a

So sometimes ah can say a new sound, aw.

> *A boy's teeth hurt, so he was sent*
> *To see the dentist. Yes he went.*
> *They told him "Open wide. Say AW."*
> *The boy did that. It was the law.*

That means that sometimes when you see little ah, it will be saying a new sound, as it says at the dentist's.

ar   aw   al

Read the words below. If the sounds you know for ah don't work (ah — cat, or get out of the way ay — cake) try aw. Join the word to the picture it matches.

car

saw

salt

Read the words below and join them to the pictures they match. Watch for little ah saying its sound at the dentist — aw.

salt

saw

ball

barn

arm

Read the words below and match them to the pictures of what they mean.

park

scarf

salt

draw

Read these words and join them to the pictures of what they mean.

car

yawn

jar

bald

Read these words and join them to the pictures they match. Watch for ah saying its sound at the dentist's — aw.

call

draw

start

fall

Read these expressions below and join them to the pictures of what they mean.

small man

tall man

hall

ball

apartment

Note to Parent: We have been teaching the child a logical system of phonics, sounding out words, with a few rules for long vowels, and vowel combinations. We will keep to those rules most of the time. However, the child will eventually have to read words that depart from those rules. It is all right for the child to experiment a little with sounds for a letter as he tries to figure out what a word says. He may see 'a' and try ah (cat), and if that didn't work, ay (cake) and if that didn't work, aw (call). This type of guessing around is a logical next step. Usually, from picture and context clues there will be nearly no confusion, but it is all right if there is some for a while. Have the child just keep trying. The word 'are', for instance, is technically a departure from strict phonics rules, but the child can be shown it now, as below.

Read the expressions below and join them to the picture they match.

a dark yard

a dog barks

Bob and Don are small

Sounds of **a**

ah says 'ah' most of the day,
Except when it says 'Get out of the way!"
Or the dentist asks, to be sure what he saw,
"Sit right down here. Open wide and say 'aw'."

Read these words and join them to the pictures of what they mean.

garden

crawl

farm

Carl

Note to Parent: The number of words your child can read has recently increased by thousands, because he/she can read the vowel combinations and the 'aw' sound of a. There are still some words the child cannot read because a few do not match the rules yet taught. But you can reprint and put around the house some of the following words for the child to read casually.

mail	laid	maid	paid	main
hail	jail	sail	tail	rain
pain	gain	train	brain	drain
stain	rail	trail	braid	afraid
bait	wait	coat	load	road
toad	soak	goal	soul	foam
roam	moan	loan	soap	toast
boat	goat	float	beads	beak
leak	streak	treat	deal	heal
meal	real	seal	steal	team
steam	stream	dream	beans	mean
clean	scream	leap	beat	heat
neat	seat	died	lied	tried
suit	glue	fruit	law	paw
saw	draw	straw	all	call
ball	fall	mall	tall	wall
stall	crawl	bar	car	far
harm	harness	Bart	barn	cart
card	dark	far	farm	harp
jar	Mars	part	park	tarts
target	carpet	all	almost	halt

Lesson 32

Crazy R

We saw how little huh would take letters and make them do funny things. He'd take the suh and shake it, make cuh go chug-a-chug, push puh into a phone.

Well little ruh was full of mischief too.

She liked to make that funny sound
you make when you are pretending to be a car engine — rrrrr.
You know the one. It sort of sounds like a lion roaring, too.
But mostly she wanted to form little cars to rev around a track.

rrrr

So she grabbed little eh and revved around, saying er er er er, like a race car.

er

And she grabbed ih, and later oh (aw), and even uh and did the same

ir   or   ur

So these pairs of letters each end up saying the very same thing — errrrrrrrrrrrrr, just like a race car.

Here are some words where this happens.
Join the word to the picture of what it means.

girl

letter

Read the words on the left and join them to the pictures they match.

river

winter

church

burn

summer

Read the words on the left and join them to the pictures of what they mean.

spider

sisters

curls

hamster

Read the words on the left and join them to the pictures of what they mean.

nurse

fur

skirt

stir

bird

Read these words and join them to the pictures of what they mean. Remember the race car 'er' sound that some pairs make.

turkey

shirt

ruler

worm

furniture

Read the pairs of words in each block below. Find the one in each set that comes FIRST in counting or in time. For instance, if you read seven and six, you would circle 'six'.

April
May

Saturday
Sunday

March
June

three
four

fifteen
seven

six
five

315

In each block below there is a recipe. Read it. Then read the list of names of food on the right. Join the recipe to the name of the food it is making.

Add hot water and stir. Let set.

cocoa

Add hot milk and stir. Drink.

jello

Boil in hot water. Eat with relish.

hot dog

316

Match the name of the store below to the picture of what it has in it.

bakery

cleaners

meat market

bookstore

kite store

Here are some words the child can now read. You can reprint some of these around the house.

purr	stir	burn	burp	nurse
curb	turkey	curl	girl	swirl
firm	perm	term	fern	turn
slurp	burst	thirst	first	worst
dirt	hurt	skirt	burner	worm
barber	doctor	actor	jumper	runner
bigger	smaller	taller	wider	fatter
thinner	older	bakery	clerk	work
after	third	Thursday	first	Saturday

Your child can also read some very long words now, by sounding them out. This may amaze you both. I would suggest you just play with a few of the ones below from time to time. If they seem very hard for the child, go back to the simpler ones, since the ones below are more like a grade two or three level. However, if the child wants to, it is certainly fun to read a few of them. You might want to prepare a few little readers using words from the lists in this volume.

afternoon	alligator	complete
athlete	altitude	carpenter
appetite	arithmetic	checkers
agreement	alphabet	contest
barbecue	blackboard	crocodile
baseball	basement	continent
buffalo	between	conductor
careful	cartoon	complain
chairlift	chimpanzee	classroom
different	disappear	director
drugstore	darkness	establish
electric	eastern	entertain
family	farther	firecracker
flavour	furniture	furnish
farewell	failure	flatter
fishy	globe	ghastly
grasshopper	green pepper	gardener
helicopter	hippopotamus	handy
hamburger	hairdresser	himself
important	increase	injury
interrupt	invite	kangaroo
ladder	lesson	literature
lantern	leapfrog	matter
mistake	minister	monster
memory	murmur	mailbox
napkin	nickel	opera

overcoat	nursery	perfect
property	probably	public
permit	preacher	posture
poverty	propeller	philosopher
pamphlet	progress	project
payment	profit	promote
peanut butter	pancake	painter
plenty	party	punishment
redbird	rooster	record store
ridicule	seesaw	sneeze
subtract	superintendent	strictly
shudder	shelter	sunshine
shamrock	shipment	shish-kabob
shopper	shotgun	simply
sprinkler	spinach	sandwich
streamline	silkworm	sleepy
September	temperature	scarlet
seagull	teeter-totter	twelfth
umbrella	understand	upstairs
valentine	whirlwind	volume
wheelchair	wonderful	yesterday

Note to Parent: Your child can now read thousands of words and has a good base for entering the school system. There is more kids could learn — like variant sounds of s (e.g., z) — but they are well on the way.

In level one he learned all the lower case letters and one sound per letter. They also learned the basic skill of sounding out words left to right.

In level two they learned the proper names of the letters, the long sounds of the vowels, the concept of vowels, the upper case letters, the consonant digraphs sh, ch, ph, gh, wh and th. They learned how to sound out consonant blends like sc, cl, fl, gl, sl, br, cr, gr. They learned variant sounds of y. They also learned vowel digraphs where the first vowel says its long sound and the second is quiet — ea, ai, oa, oe, ie, ue, ei. They have learned one very common pronunciation of ar, al, aw and the er sound of er, or, ir, and ur.

What to do from here?

1. You could review this book and then stop. Your child now has an excellent start for school.

2. You could continue with instruction of the finer points of words that are exceptions. Consult my website at http://www.telusplanet.net/public/bjaremko for more material there.

319

3. You could now introduce printing lessons for the child. I suggest you show the child how to form the letters with straight lines — l, t, k — and then the letters with curves — c, o, e — in a systematic way to show hand motions. Children can now read words they can print, so that is very motivating. Again, see my website for more information. http://www.telusplanet.net/public/bjaremko

Whatever you decide about how to proceed, you and your child deserve real congratulations. You have given your child a great head start for school, and opened up for him/her a door onto a whole new world. Some time in the next little while you will probably see your child taking that one further step, choosing to read independently.

It's amazing. You both are amazing.